Everything

You Ever Wanted To Know

About Extraordinary Sex......

Volume I

UPSO

A catalogue record of this book is available from the British Library

First Published: April 2003

ISBN: 1-84375-011-2

To order additional copies of this book please visit:
http://www.upso.co.uk/petruska.htm

Published by: UPSO
5 Stirling Road, Castleham Business Park,
St Leonards-on-Sea, East Sussex TN38 9NW UK
Tel: 01424 853349 Fax: 0870 1913991
Email: info@upso.co.uk Web: http://www.upso.co.uk

Everything

You Ever Wanted To Know

About Extraordinary Sex......

Volume I

by

Professor Petruska Clarkson, PhD, D. Litt et Phil

Consultant Philosopher and
Sexual Ecstasy Coach

What is sex?

The major purpose of sex is pleasure

Anatomy and a little bit of interesting history

Heavenly orgasmic sexual pleasure for men, women
and in-betweens

The best sex orgasms for men and for women

How best to make a man come?

How best to make a woman come?

Ecstasy – or getting high ...

If you want to make babies...

Where to go next and where to find out more...

Simple, straightforward answers from a leading International
Independent Consultant Philosopher and Sexual Ecstasy Educator.

DID YOU KNOW...?

- That women climax (from a cold start) on average in 30 seconds to 4 minutes - if they masturbate or are stimulated competently?

- That the vagina is NOT a woman's sexual organ? The anatomical equivalent (analogue) of the vagina is a man's scrotum (the skin around his balls)?

- That it is therefore as unlikely for a woman to orgasm from having a penis rubbing backwards and forwards in her vagina as it is for a man to orgasm from having his scrotum rubbed in the same way?

- That the clitoris is in fact a large organ about the size of a man's penis when flaccid - and when erect. In fact, it is anatomically accurate to say that a man's penis is an external clitoris – not vice versa. Most people have *no idea* what the clitoris really looks like? (Yet we know what our hearts, livers, kidneys etc. look like.)

- That for some 8 out of 10 women it is biologically impossible to orgasm from penile penetration alone? That is, without at least the involvement of the clit-end – the only *visible* part of the clitoris. This is statistically and anatomically NORMAL.

- That these rediscovered research findings about the whole clitoris and about human sexuality can transform your feelings and confidence about yourself as a person *and as a professional?*

- That these research findings about the clitoris and other discoveries about sexuality can completely revolutionise the way we think about and do sex?

"The right to sexual pleasure, which is a source of physical, psychological, intellectual and spiritual well-being" is the birthright of all men and all women *FOR ALL OF THEIR LIVES.*

(World Association of Sexology, 2001)

In 1974, the World Health Organisation reported: 'A growing body of knowledge indicates that problems in human sexuality are more pervasive and more important to the well-being and health of individuals in many cultures than has been previously recognized.'

Dedicated to my first lover

Contents

Preface

"A door like this has cracked open five or six times since we got up on our hind legs. It's the best possible time to be alive, when almost everything you knew is wrong." [1]

This book is for those people who are curious to learn more about **extraordinary** natural orgasmic sex and want to be updated on current developments.

Although all knowledge, like cars and alcohol, can be used or abused, I believe that *this* Sexual Knowledge should be available to everybody. If people can get accurate information in a straight way, they can take their own responsibility for the choices they make in how to live their lives.

However, knowledge alone doesn't usually achieve the desired results. Reading a book about how to play tennis isn't the same as practising with a partner and getting expert coaching for your game. The educational model I use is based on the KASH system. KASH is an acronym for *Knowledge, Attitudes, Skills and Habits*.

KNOWLEDGE needs to be accompanied by changed ATTITUDES and SKILLS training. These take much more quality investment of time and resources in expert coaching - the price and duration of it only depending on whether **you** want to eventually play in Championship League or remain forever in Third Division. Or eventually get to qualify as an Erotic Black Belt Master and Teacher or not.

Neither attitude change or skills training will achieve the sexual desired results either *unless* the player also, of course, *practises* the skills they have learnt until they become unconsciously competent HABITS. Just like once you've been driving a car for a couple of years. Or becoming

---

[1] Stoppard, T., (1993) Arcadia, pp. 47 - 48, Faber and Faber, London.

competent and confident in how to drive a golf ball down the tee. And that's only the start of 'reducing your handicap!')

Because 'genuine competency' *at anything* **includes** the SELF-CONFIDENCE that you are competent. As well as other people, such as your BELOVED, or your boss, also agreeing that you are competent. Or excellent. (That's why the Clarkson's Institute's certification system – or the seven coloured 'belts' *includes* your BELOVED'S feedback.)

When winners feel inside themselves like losers or impostors in any field, they are suffering false competence (or 'pseudo-competency') as I have termed it technically. (See *'Overcoming the secret fear of failure – the Achilles Syndrome'* re-published in 2003 by Vega.) Even people who are considered by *others* to be wonderful LOVERS can experience such a lack of inner self-confidence in their own erotic competency. This can be fixed with expert help.

But, there are some people who believe themselves to be wonderful LOVERS, but nobody else who has experienced their loving, think so. This is when losers feel inside themselves like winners. These guys are *really* in trouble because sooner or later Life **will** 'find them out'.

An example of this was a man who pursued me very actively me for a long time. He claimed - and fully believed himself - that he was one of the world's greatest LOVERS. My woman's intuition said **not**. (Takes only a man's first physical pass to establish this. That's why the first pass is *so* important.) So he thought he'd finally convince me when he said that I could get his last BELOVED on the mobile phone and ask her myself. She would speak to me.

Being an inveterate researcher who rarely passes on a opportunity to ask somebody an interesting question, I duly phoned and asked her about her own personal experience of this man as a lover. This is exactly, word by word, what she said: *"He's a real randy bastard, but when we have sex, he only wriggles about for a little bit before he comes."*

She *might* have been lying. However, over three decades as a leading international professional in the fields of psychology, counselling, psychoanalysis and psychotherapy I have worked with, researched, written about, taught and supervised thousands of people - many of them sex therapists or couples counsellors. I have therefore come to know of the lives of hundreds of thousands of people. What that woman said is true for most of them.

Naturally, for this book, I also draw on my own very varied experience of being a sexual person for all of my life. Personally, I have been in three long-term happy and successful relationships of more than a decade each.

My first husband and I trained in Tantra Yoga under the tutelage of a Guru. We were in an 'open marriage' for 10 good years – just before that kind of relationship become fashionable.

A decade with a woman – just before Lesbianism become fashionable - was followed by a mutually monogamous marriage to a man 20 years younger than me – just before that kind of relationship became fashionable.

I have also had the benefit of an 18-month period of the ancient practice of chosen celibacy - until a hunky 19-year-old Italian returned me to the world of sexual ecstasy - via 'the international language of the body'.

I am currently a *plural* – in several relationships at the same time – just like one in seven men and one in eleven women in the UK. Whether it's 'in' or 'out', it's what's happening now.

However, in the last few years I have realised that most – if not all – of my professional learning and training was not only ***wrong*** in terms of human sexuality, but actually limiting and ***damaging*** to human well-being.

That's why I now do NOT do my 'sex work' as a 'counsellor' or 'sex therapist', but as a **Sexual Ecstasy Educator** and **Love Coach.**

I think it is ethically wrong to 'treat' human beings for 'sexual dysfunction' or 'sexual problems' when these are mostly created by lack of education and actual misinformation from so-called 'authorities'. Or simple financial greed. Minor examples are the financial exploitation of men (2/3 according to one research study) who are concerned about the length or hardness or duration of their erections. *None* of which are particularly relevant to multiple ecstatic orgasms for both men and women.

For another example, British research published **this year** [2] reports:

Experienced by up to 43% of the female adult population, female sexual dysfunction [FSD] is a condition with high latent, but low realized, potential . From the onset of symptoms to diagnosis of FSD, patients withdraw at multiple points from the treatment flow. Fulfilling FSD's **commercial potential** *will hinge* **critically** *upon translating patient potential into a diagnosed and treated population. (my emphasis)*

Think and feel about this labelling of statistically and anatomically normal female sexuality as "Female Sexual Dysfunction", FSD for short, which "commercial potential" needs to be exploited. This is of course also and furthermore supporting the labelling of almost half of adult women as suffering from **psychiatric** disease – according to the DSM criteria. Check it out!

The amazingly fast and positive results of my philosophical sex work with other people in the last few years have proven that many, if not most of, these so-called 'sexual problems' disappear quickly, easily and with the most gratifying reliable orgasms given (a) a little bit of truthful information and (b) a willing LOVE PRACTICE partner.

Consistent practice with mentoring from an Expert Love Coach then leads to further possibilities for life-time improvement in the quality of sex you do. And the quality of your relationships. And the quality of your Life.

Just like any other sport or art form, of course, natural in-born **erotic talent** makes a difference. Some people seem to be born erotically gifted.

---

[2] Strategic Perspectives: Female Sexual Dysfunction. Are physicians and patients ready for a female Viagra? August, 2002. Datamonitor. Reference Code DMHC 1797 p. 1.

However, *any* body can **achieve more** of their inherent erotic potential for giving and receiving sexual ecstasy – if they care enough to devote some real time, energy and resources to it.

Personally, these last years of personal discovery and intensive, scientific, literature and 'real world research' have led me now to experience ecstasy from sex regularly, often and with the most profound spiritual sense of WORSHIP for the miracle of LIFE.

This book is merely a *beginning* statement of what I've been finding out. I am publishing it in this way because of overwhelming popular demand for it to be available quickly to as many people as possible.

Men who like making love with men or women who like making love with women may also find it useful, but really this is *primarily* written for the millions of dissatisfied men and frustrated women who would like to make ecstatic love to each other – and have just never been shown how.

I would like to make your further journey into Sex Heaven less expensive, safer and even more wonderful than anything you have yet experienced.

It's up to you how you use it. Reading it once is fine. But re-reading it many times is better. Every time you will have a deeper understanding of what is being communicated to you in the spaces *between the words*.

DISCLAIMER: (Refer to p.46) Of course, *always* remember to check everything you are doing, or plan to do, which may affect your health with your **General Medical Practitioner** before taking any risk whatsoever. But, also check out the sex information given to doctors (refer to page 32 and page 48)

! **This sign means caution - be care-full, be aware**

* **This sign means take notice, there are almost always exceptions**

? **This sign means think further about it, wonder why, speculate further**

SEXUALITY SURVEY[3]

1. My preferred frequency of sexual intercourse is

    (a) every day
    (b) 2 – 3 times a week
    (c) 2 to 3 times a month
    (d) at least once in my lifetime

2. The diagram below illustrates

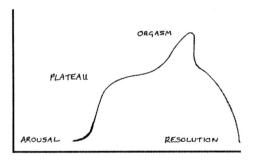

    (a) the male sexual response cycle
    (b) the female breast during arousal
    (c) the Dow Jones Industrial Average for January

3. Vaginal lubrication is

    (a) necessary every 6,000 miles
    (b) only for greasers
    (c) the female parallel to male pre-cum

4. Autoeroticism is

    (a) making it in a car
    (b) a lube job
    (c) masturbation

---

[3] After Fabick, Stephen D. , Sexuality Survey in Ellenbogen, G.C., (ed) (1987) *Oral Sadism and the Vegetarian Personality,* New York: Bruner/Mazel, p. 126 – 127 Substantially modified and added by Petruska Clarkson.

5. Homo sapiens is the only species which has intercourse face-to-face

   (a) true
   (b) false
   (c) both of the above
   (d) I don't care what those homos do

6. People who put cottage cheese in their pants

   (a) excite me
   (b) are Republicans or Tories
   (c) are health nuts
   (d) are disgusting

7. Sexual intercourse should occur within the context of

   (a) marriage
   (b) honesty and mutual caring
   (c) the backseat of an old Chevy

8. Testicular tumescence is

   (a) fun
   (b) a rock group
   (c) penile erection

9. When my mother reminded me to wear my rubbers, she meant

   (a) my wellies
   (b) my prophylactics
   (c) both of the above

10. Foreplay is

    (a) group sex with four people
    (b) a golf term
    (c) a prelude to sexual intercourse
    (d) a consolation prize given by a bored man to an orgasm-starved
        woman

11. The clitoris is

   (a) "The **what** ?"
   (b) A holiday island in Greece
   (c) A woman's pea-size bump down there
   (d) The anatomical predecessor of the male penis and **equivalent** to it in size.

12. The G-spot is

   (a) Somewhere in the Himalayas
   (b) Like ghosts and virgins. You hear about them, but you never meet one
   (c) The anatomical equivalent of the male prostrate which can easily be felt to protrudes into the vagina, but only when a woman's whole clitoris is erect.

13. Female ejaculation is

   (a) a myth
   (b) a fantasy
   (c) the only real evidence that a woman isn't faking
   (d) the exact equivalent of male ejaculation – only without sperm

14. Male multiple orgasms

   (a) Are a myth
   (b) Are a fantasy
   (c) can only be achieved by becoming a Yoga master
   (d) a reality

15. My favourite sexual fantasy involves

   (a) Visualising my rabbi (or the pope) eating a banana
   (b) Peering at a sausage and doughnut strolling through Central Park
   (c) Making it with the author of a sexual survey.

Chapter 1

What is sex?

"Sex contains all, bodies, souls,
Meanings, proofs, purities, delicacies, results, promulgations,
Songs, commands, health, pride, the maternal mystery, the seminal milk,
All hopes, benefactions, bestowals, all the passions, loves, beauties, delights
of the earth,
All the governments, judges, gods, followed persons of the earth,
These are contained in sex as parts of itself and justifications of itself." [4]

Having got your attention in one way or another, I now want to talk to your inner child. No matter how young - or how old - you are.

Do you remember the first time you found out about the very best feelings in your body? You know, those weird and wonderful sensations that feel like you're in a kind of heaven of happiness? You may have even felt like you're going to pass right out because of its wonderfulness? When your body first felt like a sea or a waterfall or a thunderstorm or a sky-full of *fireworks*?

This is the very best secret about your body. And because it is such a good and precious secret people don't tell you about it. Most people discover this hidden invisible sexual treasure all by themselves. Just like I know you did. But you don't have to tell me about it, because I know it's very very difficult to put into words. *All the most wonderful magic things in Life are very difficult to put into words.*

ORGASM is only one word for it which many people use. It is the strongest nicest feeling of all the feelings that a body can have. It is intense. It is *extreme*. It is concentrated Life Energy so strong that sometimes you can almost faint from it.

---

[4] Whitman, W. (1980) 'A Woman Waits for Me, *Leaves of Grass*, New York: New American Library. (pp 98-106)

- 1 -

It's almost painful it can be so strong, and powerful. But it is also beautiful and happy at the same time. You feel like you're just about dying when you come. At the same time you feel more alive than you can ever imagine. It's like opposites becoming the same. Intensely. Extremely.

But you remember. You remember right now the first time you discovered the very best secret about your body - all by yourself. The good feelings from touching yourself between your legs or rubbing yourself up against something. And even if you don't remember, your body probably does.

Sometimes other people interfere with a child discovering this sexual secret all by themselves and spoil it. That's mostly bad, because it is much more fun to find it out for yourself. About orgasms.

Or somebody says you mustn't do it and then you feel bad about the most wonderful secret of your body. That's stupid. It's better not to listen to such people.

How can such a wonderful secret with which you can make yourself feel good be a bad thing to do? That just doesn't make sense. God or nature or evolution (people call it by different names) wouldn't have put such a wonderful secret in our bodies if it was bad would it?

It is in everybody's body in the whole world. No matter what they look like. It is a good way to make ourselves relax, or go to sleep, or to make ourselves feel the wonderful miracle of Life's energy singing right between our legs.

And it's going to be there for you for all of your life – no matter how old you get. Very old people can have orgasms as long as they *live* until the day they die.

People who have no arms or legs or who are paralyzed can have orgasms until the day they die. No matter what other people think. There's a very useful book by Dr. Tuppy Owens on this subject. It is called '*Practical Suggestions*' which is good to read in this context.

I think and feel that the MIRACLE OF ORGASMS is Nature's medicine for some of the pain and suffering we have to go through as people on this planet.

Of course, a child mustn't do sex in front of other people. It is a private thing like going to the toilet. (And we all know that we often get good body feelings from going to the toilet.) But, when people grow up, they sometimes like to do it together or watch each other do it. That can make it even more wonderful.

So wonderful that you must be careful with whom you share it – just like any other good secret. Sometimes other people won't understand sex and try to spoil it for you. Don't pay any attention to them – as long as you don't upset them by practising your body's best secret in front of them.

Some people discover their body's most wonderful secret when they are just babies. Some people discover it when they're children. Some people discover it much later in their lives. This is sad, because they miss out on the wonderful feelings that are always there for anybody any time they want to feel it, in private. You can't do too much of it because your body will tell you what is too much quite quickly.

Too much is when you get sore. You must stop and take a rest or do something different *before* you get sore. That's the only other thing you have to remember. But a body can take a walloping big load of natural sex ecstasy before it gets sore. So, don't worry, be happy in private as much as you want to, but without getting sore.

There are as many ways of having these wonderful sex feelings as there are different people in the world. Each one of us is slightly different. Just like our fingerprints.

Some people rub themselves against a pillow or a toy between their legs. Some people touch themselves until they find the best way to make their body's sex happiness. Some people squeeze their legs together tightly or make their thighs like a bird's beating wings in order to come. There are a million trillion ways to make sex orgasms.

You have probably already found the way that is best for you. You don't have to tell anybody – but you can if you want to. Lovers often show each other how they do it, so they can learn the other person's best body secrets and make sex even better when they do it together.

! Beware of anyone who tells you what kind of orgasms *your* body should have. (And that includes me.) Every body is different and you yourself are the world expert on your own body. Think and feel for yourself to test out whether anybody else's ideas are true for **you.**

* There is a great deal of bullshit talked and taught about sexual pleasure. We all have to be very careful about where we get our information from and whether it is the best, most truthful, *current* information. And we have to keep up with new discoveries. Much further research is needed. Particularly in our own bodies.

? Where did *you* get your sex education from? Your parents? Other kids? School? Pornographic movies? Magazines? Sex Manuals? Please send me your answers and some examples if you want to help with finding out what is going on with sex in our world.

Chapter 2

The purpose of sex

'There is a kind of food
not taken in through the mouth:
Bits of knowing that nourish love.
The body and the human personality form a cup.
Every time you meet someone, something is poured in.' [5](Rumi)

DOING ECSTATIC SEX TOGETHER IS NATURE'S BEST WAY
OF GIVING HUMAN BEINGS COMFORT AND HAPPINESS
FROM OUR BODIES. Mind you, animals and insects do it too. Some
animals do it a lot, alone or with each other. Lots of animals make sex
with other creatures of the same sex and in all kinds of wonderfully
different ways.

I have heard that some monkeys called *Bonobos* do sex almost all the
time. Also dolphins, who are very clever creatures, like sex a lot. I think
that the cleverer creatures are, the more they want comfort and
happiness and the better they get at making it in different ways.

I personally think and feel that Nature (or God) wants us to have
heavenly sex orgasms as much as we can to make up for all the suffering,
pain and confusion we get in life. It's kind of to balance things out a
little.

Birds and bees are not good examples, because they don't practice
making sex happiness as much as the Bonobo monkeys or the *dolphins*
do. I don't know why. Perhaps birds and bees are not as clever as us and
the Bonobos and the dolphins – or maybe we just don't know yet how
they do it.

---

⁵ Rumi

Find a piece from a school book explaining sex and compare that with what I'll be writing here. If you want to, please send me a copy. It's all part of the research.

So, instead of studying birds and bees, we humans must study the Bonobos and the dolphins to see if we can learn anything about making more sex body happiness more often.

Anyway, even without studying the Bonobos and the dolphins, human children figure sex orgasm happiness out for themselves pretty well all on their own. And as they grow older they start figuring it out with other people. Sometimes with other boys, sometimes with other girls, sometimes with somebody of the 'opposite sex'.

Sometimes adults get in on children's sexual pleasure, but this is wrong. It is called *"child abuse"* because the grown-up can hurt the child and spoil their sex body happiness for later.

Grown-ups should make sex play with other grown-ups because they are stronger and made for each other. Grown-ups who interfere with children finding their own sexual body happiness are silly and sick. Such adults need help from feelings doctors (psychologists) until they find sexual playmates of their own size.

Grownups can play sexual daddies, boys and girls; or mommies and boys for orgasms. Many adult people also like sexual dressing-up games like at Carnival, Halloween or in Pantomime where men dress up as women or bad army generals in boots. Women can also dress up as men or wicked witches. Many adults also like to pretend that they are school-teachers and pupils or doctors and nurses and patients or even pirates and slaves for sexual ecstasy.

Just like children, grownups love to play fun games. But grownups *deliberately* add **orgasms** to their sexual games. They can play tying up games like with ropes or blindfolds; *pretend* scary scenes like from the movies such as being kidnapped or tortured; tell each other fantastic sexy stories; act out interesting scenes from history or space travel with each other in full costume or masks; play at being ponies like in piggyback games; make sexy use of swings or balloons or bathrooms or sploshy food; or do an Adult version of Dungeons and Dragons. All the things that children like to do and many more – just with sex orgasms thrown in.

Because adults are *grown-up* they **must** know how to play orgasmic sex games safely and not damage anybody – if they are healthy. Not sick or bad or stupid. (I define 'stupid' as not using the brains you've got.) Grown-ups can play these good sexual orgasm games with each other as much as they like if everybody involved says yes. But adults are not to do it with real children – or in front of real children.

It's very easy to *pretend* you're bigger or smaller or younger or older than you really are once you're grownup. That way both people can choose whatever they want to in orgasm sex and nobody gets forced to choose only one way.

If you're still a child you will know when some adult is trying to spoil your future sex body happiness as soon as they touch you on your body where your swimsuit usually covers your body up - or if they give you wet kisses and try to put their tongue in your mouth.

Or maybe the grown-up wants you to put your hands or mouth on the parts of their body which is usually covered up. If this happens, call for help or tell some good adult immediately.

This grown up person who is trying to spoil your own sexual body fun needs to be helped by other adults, not by you (if you are a child). No matter what they say. Even if it is somebody you love.

If you *really* love them, you will try to get them the help they need by telling other adults about it. And you will not let anybody spoil your own sex body happiness because another time they will be sorry that they did. So think about this and be careful.

The same is true for grown-ups. Some people want to interfere with your body fun and just make a grab for you or force you – even if you don't want to make sex play with them. This is also a crime because it is bad to make anybody do something with sex that they don't want to do. Such adult people also need urgent help.

And if they don't go and get the proper help for themselves and stop forcing people to have sex with them, they must go and stay in prison.

ALWAYS TELL SOMEBODY YOU TRUST ABOUT SUCH THINGS. No matter how young or how old you are. **Don't keep anybody's bad secrets.** Bad secrets need telling quickly because otherwise they just get worse. Just like a person with an illness must get to a doctor or a hospital quickly otherwise they get even sicker and somebody may die. THE PURPOSE OF SEX IS PLEASURE.

! People can pick up diseases from sex with other people just the same as from food or from other things we put in our bodies. This information is widely available e.g. from your school or your doctor. Make sure you get somebody to explain how these health risks may affect *you*.

* Don't let this put you off having many wonderful sex orgasms. There are *hundreds* of ways of having wonderful orgasms that cannot possibly make you ill or cause death. Find out all you can about these risk-free ways.

? **Remember** that information about sex, like about everything else, is changing all the time. How do you keep yourself up to date with the latest news on this? I'll be updating this book every time I find better or truer information. *You can help by letting me know what you find out – and how.*

Chapter 3

Anatomy and a little bit of interesting history

*"We began
as a mineral. We emerged into plant life
and into the animal state, and then into being human,
and always we have forgotten our former states,
except in early spring when we slightly recall
being green again."* [6]

We all know what a penis looks like because it is carried on the outside of a man's body. And we can see it on sculptures of males who are not wearing fig-leaves, for example, Michelangelo's famous David. The penis is the sexual organ of the male human being and is *on average* 5 inches (12.5 cm) long. **The penis is the body centre of a man's sexual ecstasy.**

The clitoris is on the inside a woman's body with just a little end of it sticking out. We usually ***don't see*** even the visibly sticky-out part of it on sculptures of women. The rest is inside. The clitoris is the sexual organ of the female human being and is *on average* 4 and a half inches (12cm) long. (This is simply because many women's bodies are smaller than most men's bodies.) **The clitoris is the body centre of a woman's orgasmic sexual ecstasy.**

Here is what a clitoris looks like if seen from the left. This illustration comes from a medical textbook published in **1844** by a German doctor. He called the clitoris *"this sexual heart"*. Isn't that a beautiful name for a woman's sexual organ?

---

[6] Rumi

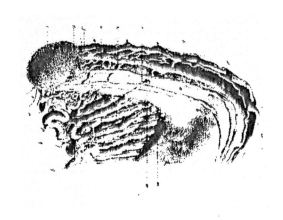

Kobelt Clitoris

You will notice that the clitoris looks very like a penis. That's no surprise, because anatomically they are the *same* organs. The woman's body came first in evolution, so she has a XX chromosome arrangement. A man's chromosome arrangement is a variation on the woman's, XY.

The penis is therefore, in anatomical fact, an **externally carried clitoris.** You may know this, also from the fact that the sex of a foetus (a boy or a girl or an in-between) can only be established comparatively late it its development. THE CLITORIS AND THE PENIS ARE THE SAME ORGAN. What is their function?

The penis and the clitoris are both made for us by Nature for having heavenly sex orgasms. The clitoris is inside the woman's body above and around her vagina over the pelvic bone and goes down the tops of her thighs to each side.

This arrangement keeps her clitoris safe and protected from damage. So she never has to worry about not having as many sex orgasms as she wants for all of her life. It's too bad for the guys that a penis on the outside of your body can get hurt or sick quite easily.

Here is a more modern drawing of the clitoris which my friends and I made to show that, looking at it from the front (same as we can now, with modern technology look at pictures of a foetus inside a woman's tummy). It looks a little like a wishbone with the top part curving around toward the front:

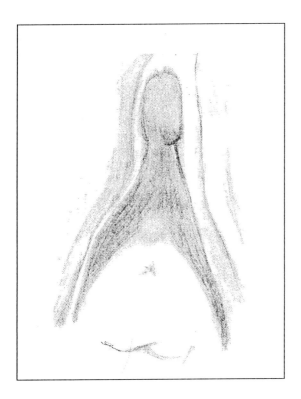

Wishbone shape of clitoris
©PHYSIS 2002

This drawing is based on the scientific work of Dr Helen O'Connell, a world expert from Melbourne Hospital in Australia. She commented on this drawing: "*This is fine. It is accurate and looks good. It lacks a view of the length of the clitoral body or the exact relationship between the bulbs and the vaginal wall. To do this you have to show the clitoris as a lateral or oblique view. But this is a good picture.*"

If you want to look at colour pictures of the clitoris *in real human flesh* you can look up Dr. O'Connell's photographs on the worldwide web at the International Journal of Urology (1998).

Just in case you can't get to read the exciting story of Helen's work and see its grand colour illustrations yet, here is another drawing of the clitoris: This time in three dimensions. I think it looks much more like the heart symbol that we use on greetings cards for example, than the real heart which has quite a different shape – as you know. The clitoris looks, from this angle, like an upside down heart.

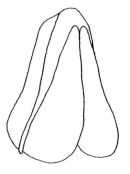

Tulip-shaped clitoris

©PHYSIS 2002

So, you see, the clitoris is like a pyramid or tulip-shaped organ which any girl or woman can feel inside her body as **the centre of her orgasms** - just like the stomach is the centre of the body's digestive system. In girls, the clitoris is smaller than in grown-up women of course. That's why the best body happiness in sex comes when the clitoris has grown to its full size.

I think Nature's plan is to give us practice when we're young so that we can be ready for the greatest sex body-happiness when we're at least sixteen years old. That's when our country's law allows us to start sex-playing with the other adults and nobody will be committing a crime and have to go to prison for it. Unless of course, they threaten or force somebody.

You've probably seen or played with the little sticky-out part of it, but that's only **the clit-end.** Clitoris means 'little hill' in olden Greek.

This tiny little bit is the only visible part of the clitoris. The Italian Dr. Mateo Colombo named *Amor Veneris, vel Dulcedo Apeletur in 1558.* These Latin words mean something like: "**The Sweetness of Venus**" – after the Roman Goddess of Love. (She was called **Aphrodite** by the Greeks and we get the word aphrodisiac from her name.)

Dr. Colombo thought that he had 'discovered' that some grown women got ill from not having sex orgasms. So then he went around and cured these women by stroking their clitorises with his hand and then - of course - they felt better. Indeed, they felt wonderful! All their depression just disappeared. There's a great book by an Argentinean writer Azhazi called *"The Anatomist"* which tells his story - and how the Catholic Church tried to shut him up.

Now, some doctors have always known that **the clit-end** is only a tiny fraction of the real clitoris which is *at least as big* as a penis. So it would be better called "**THE BIG MOUNTAIN**".

Many people think and teach that sex is when a man puts his penis in a woman's vagina, pokes around in it and then spouts his sperm into it. Sadly, they are wrong. This is just the best way for making babies. A lot of scientific research tells us this is *not* the best way to make SEX HEAVEN for most people – especially not for most women.

See, Nature made **the vagina** like a useful fleshy elastic bag to keep menstrual blood in. Of course, it can also sometimes expand just like a balloon to help even a baby who weighs eight pounds inside the woman's body into the world. If the vagina was full of nerve-endings I think nobody would ever give birth at all because it would hurt far too much!

So, thank God, most of the vagina doesn't have the nerve-endings to create even more pain in childbirth. Of course, anatomically, that means that **the vagina also doesn't have the nerve-endings for creating the heavenly sexual feelings of orgasms.**

Two-thirds of a woman's vagina is like anaesthetised. At least since 1844 doctors have known that you can operate on the vagina *without* anaesthetic. So, **no** nerve-endings *there* to speak of, for pain. Or for pleasure.

The reason the first third of the front of the vagina (around the entrance) can sometimes feel so *delicious* is because that part has the clitoris organ running around beneath it. Just study this picture:

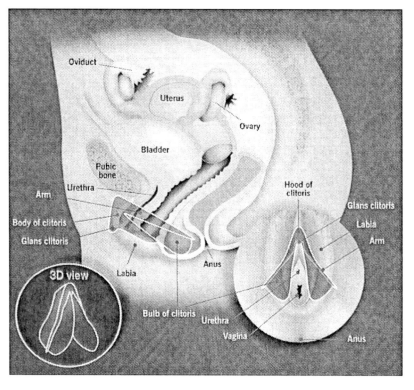

New Scientist

So that's why, as long as a man has a penis long enough to just get it inside the woman's vagina and put the sperm in, *the size of anybody's cock can't possibly matter.* Not for baby-making, nor for sex heaven. So it's obvious Nature (or God) thought of this when organising how babies are to be made. Whatever the sizes.

! Don't believe *anybody* - particularly not doctors, counsellors or 'sex manuals' - who tell you anything different **until** you have checked out all the very best facts for yourself with scientific experts you can really trust to know their business – and who try to keep up-to-date with new medical information and independent research about human bodies.

* Some people, just like many animals, have creative variations of the common o'garden two major types of sexual organs (penises *or* clitorises). If these sexual organ varieties are healthy, these people too can have heavenly orgasms - in many ways - just the same as the anybody else.

? Do you want to contribute to a better, happier world? Then go and ask you GP to show you a picture of the clitoris and to explain how it works in intercourse. **Please** e-mail me what he or she says or does. *Your (anonymous, if you like) answer will be valued as part of a world-wide experiment in sex education for health and relationship well-being.*

Chapter 4

Orgasmic sexual ecstasy and its opponents

'When you gaze at a couple and wonder
What trait makes him 'him' and her 'her',
Beware for it's easy to blunder
And be false in what you aver.

Some creatures change sex before teatime,
Some others find two sexes dull,
And that virile male fish has no free time –
He's got all his kiddies to lull.

When it comes to the topic of gender,
Mother Nature's been having some fun.
Take nothing for granted! Remember,
You won't find any rules – not a one!'
(Judson)

As we saw in the previous chapter, the excitement and joy-feelings which a woman can often seem to feel in her vagina comes from *the first third* of the bag-like cavity as we feel into it with our fingers - because it is there all close to the real BIG pleasure organ called *the* CLITORIS.

That's no empty hole like the vagina. That's the real thing! A MOUNTAIN. The clitoris' only job on earth is Heaven-making. *Not* baby-making. Science has proved that the clitoris is, in fact, the only physical organ in the human body *exclusively* designed by Nature for pleasure, for good orgasm feelings and for body-happiness.

Built-in NATURAL ecstasy without expensive and dangerous drugs.
It doesn't cost any money at all! And furthermore, it's without any risk

of making unwanted babies. So we see from the anatomical evidence that (a) the vagina is for making babies and (b) the whole clitoris is specially and exclusively for heavenly orgasmic sexual pleasure. Wow! Ain't that grand?

But you've probably figured that out for yourself already. It's just that so many people have been taught that all sex must be baby-making or pretend baby-making sex. This is when a man puts his penis in a woman's vagina and pushes in and out till his sperm juice comes out. (However, as the statistics keep showing us, this is not the way 8 out of 10 real women come to orgasm heaven.)

The penis, a man's sexual organ, has to do *double* duty. Obviously he can have heavenly orgasms from it, but he also has to use it to pee ('urinating'). But a woman's peeing comes from her urethra which is anatomically separate.

A woman's sexual organ, THE CLITORIS, is the only organ in the human body *exclusively* dedicated to giving her orgasm ecstasies. (I don't know why life is sometimes so unfair.)

Indeed, *this fact* led to a very famous row on Mount Olympus – the palace of the ancient Greek Gods. These gods were the *celebrities* of that time. Zeus (who was like the Greek Elvis, The King) and his wife Hera, got into an argument about who gets the best orgasms – a man or a woman.

So, the story goes that in the end Zeus consulted Tiresias - who was the wisest man he could find in the world of that time. And Tiresias told him that a woman has **nine times** the sexual pleasure than a man can possibly have. (Tiresias could speak from personal experience because he was a transsexual.)

So, Hera got so cross with Tiresias for letting out *The Great Women's Secret*, she went and blinded him. (Those Greek God celebrities could do just about whatever they wanted.) Anyhow we know that Zeus, whatever his many affairs with other women or other goddesses, kept going back to Hera. That's married men for you.

The factual point is the G-spot. The G-spot (or *Grafenburg* spot[*]) named after the *guy* who 'discovered' it, is the little bean-sized part of **the whole clitoris** that sticks out into the vaginal cavity. However it only protrudes like that when the woman is sexually aroused. (Some people call sexual arousal being 'randy' or 'horny'. Personally I like calling it 'rutty'.)

A female human is sexually aroused of course, when her clitoris is not flaccid or limp anymore, but has become engorged with blood and swelled up to almost 3 times its usual size. Just like a man's penis does when it becomes erect. Many girls and women can feel their clitorises erect inside themselves. It's like a tense but pleasant tight sensation all *around* the vagina itself and spreading into the thighs.

If you're a girl, when next you feel really *sexy* in private, put your finger inside your vagina and then feel, on the tummy side of the vagina, from the inside of the cavity, about one third into the vagina at the top, the famous wonderful G-spot of your whole beautiful clitoris organ.

Some people say they can't find it. The simple reason for that is because they're looking when the woman hasn't got 'a hard-on'. The lady's clitoris *must be erect* in order for it to protrude enough into the vagina to be easily felt with fingers.

A darling lover of mine described it as '*a little rounded velvet cushion*'. The texture of it feels ridged, similar to the surface of a walnut - or to how your fingers feel after you've been in the bath too long. The bit of erect erotic body-tissue you can feel with your fingers, located just before you feel the hollow behind it, is the G-spot of the whole clitoris. This is **the peak** of the whole clitoris mountain.

Anyone can see and feel this for themselves on an anatomically correct model of a woman's genitals like the famous Jenteal. I have one in my consulting room where women can learn about themselves and where men can do hands-on practice with it under my instruction.

---

[*] See Kahn Ladas, A., Whipple, B. and Perry, John D. (1983) *The G Spot and other recent discoveries about human sexuality*, London: Corgi.

I would recommend every school and every home to have a Jenteal too so that *everybody* can learn how women work sexually right from the beginning.

By understanding and practising on a Jenteal, all human beings can learn how to properly love a woman's body to heavenly orgasms if they wanted to. And of course women can learn how to best love their own bodies right from when they first feel those delicious heavenly before-orgasm sexy feelings between their legs.

Every female body has this NATURAL ORGASM **REFLEX** - unless it has been damaged by some disease. *It's a basic natural physiological reflex* of the body. It's the same as when a doctor hits you on the kneecap with a small instrument, your leg will jerk up and out.

Handle even a little part of the whole clitoris in the right way, and any woman will orgasm. Just think of Doctor Colombo going around in sixteenth century Italy and healing women from their 'melancholy unto death'. What was his technique? I'm going to quote a piece from Andahazi's book to give you the flavour of it:

Matteo Colombo "took hold of the strange organ between his thumb and index finger, and with the index finger of his other hand he began gently caressing the red and engorged gland. He then observed that every muscle in the patient's body, up to them completely relaxed, tensed suddenly and involuntarily, while the organ grew somewhat in size and throbbed with brief contractions.

'It moves!' cried out Bertino. [His assistant]

'Silence! Or do you want the abbot to find out?

Mateo Colombo continued to rub the protuberance between his fingers, like someone rubbing a twig against in stone in order to make fire. Suddenly, as if he had finally managed to light a spark, Ines' entire body shook with one great convulsion that made her lift her hips and balance her body on her head and heels, like an arch. Gradually, her hips began to move to the regular rhythms of the anatomist's fingers. Her breathing became agitated, her heart was racing in her chest, and suddenly her entire body glistened with sweat. The anatomist's ministrations were provoking each of the dreadful symptoms that assaulted her every night. And yet, though the patient remained unconscious, it did not seem as if the proceedings were making her suffer exactly.….."

And Colombo was only relating manually to the clit-end - the *visible* part of 'the organ which he called the 'sweetness of Venus' or 'the seat of the patient's love and pleasure'. Matteo Colombo found that when he did *that* his female patients would show themselves *"eager to satisfy me in whatever it is I might desire.…And such surrender does not depend on any attribute save that of knowing how to manipulate it with craft and cunning.……."*

How to manipulate the little clit-end? It's no mystery at all. Just the way you most like your penis manipulated - with loving and varied attention to it. It's the *same* kind of flesh, just arranged in two wings, as I've shown you. You can't see it with the naked eye. But boy, can you **feel** it with your naked flesh!

Diseases of the clitoris, as far as I've been able to find out to date, are *exceptionally* rare. Unless a girl has had the misfortune of having had an obstetrician or surgeon operate on her who did not know what they were doing. Or deliberately cut it or mutilated it.

There are millions of women in the world today who *have to have* their clitorises cut up for various reasons. Most commonly to cut off the clit-end. I think and feel this is very **cruel.** Fortunately, because of the anatomical structure of the whole clitoris, *this does NOT stop women who have had their clit-ends amputated having heavenly sex orgasms.*

I know this **for sure,** because some of the women who have been so genitally mutilated for cultural reasons, have personally told me that they are having heavenly sex orgasms. Knowing about the whole clitoris, I was not in the least surprised

But, **please** don't tell those ignorant clit-end amputators this. You never know what these guys may decide to do next to extinguish female orgasmic sexual ecstasy - if they have *this* information!

Which brings me to our own home-grown clit-end amputating fascist – Dr. Freud. Let me tell you a little-known fact. Some women who were psychoanalysed by Freud deliberately chose to have their clitorises surgically cut up. Why? Because *he* said they **must not** have sexual excitement from their clitorises. What women will do for masterful men!

> "In psychoanalytic theories the woman comes out of her encounter with the phallus, and consequently with the law of the father, as castrated. But castrated of what? Not of the phallus, because she does not have one, but of her of her own sexuality… but one could say that her deprivation takes place at the symbolic level, where in Lacanian terms she is the loser by definition." (**Ms.** Benvenuto and Mr. Kennedy, 1986, p. 194).

Well at least that's honest. What bothers *me* is that the men are *also* losers if all they gain are orgasmically and 'therapeutically' sexually **castrated** women. All the real world evidence shows that most psychologically healthy men would actually prefer sexually satisfied and potent women as lovers and beloveds. What do *you* think?

So, all psychoanalysts and counsellors and therapists **even today in our 21st century world** who use Freud's 'theories' about human sexuality are actually practising their 'therapies' based on very damaging lies. And then the women who come to them for help, feel VERY bad about themselves. (And the men are miserable too.) I think and feel that this is also very cruel.

These 21st century practitioners of today may not be actively supporting real surgical amputations of women's clit-ends - as Freud himself did. However, they are actually performing *functional* cliterodectomies on their female patients.

'The woman', according to such psychoanalysts as quoted in the example above, 'does not have a phallus', but she has to be 'castrated' of her sexuality on top of it! According to them. Hey people, wake up!

There is only one 'phallus'. And **every *body*** has one!

And just like in other parts of the world, the women psychoanalysts of the West are often the most eager to inflict their own past and ongoing suffering on younger or more vulnerable women. (Unconsciously, I hope!)

Psycho-practitioners of such 'persuasions' sacrifice the truth on the altar of 'schoolist' adherence to false theories or ideological 'approaches'. Such misguided practitioners (who cannot think for themselves) might as well be cutting up the female clitoris *themselves* with their own hands or words.

How? Because from their 'expert position', of being the 'qualified helping professional', they are consistently denying the reality of female sexual anatomy and orgasmic experience in their patients. Ignoring the clitoris - and women's sexual ecstasy - out of existence. (Just like in the famous Gray's anatomy book. And most others.)

Well, it keeps the 'patients' – especially the very large proportion of most such private therapy practices who are **women** - forking out money to these psycho-practitioners. For as long as these patients keep suffering from 'lack' of desire', 'sexual dysfunction', 'genital immaturity' and all the other pathologising labels we professionals can hang on people to keep them sick. And *coming*. To therapy.

Even ***fervent Freud fans*** such as the authors I quote below, admit that Freud made a BIG mistake about the clitoris:

> *It is almost inconceivable that Freud was not aware of the orthodox views of contemporary anatomists and physiologists, who had, from well before the early nineteenth century, demonstrated that the clitoris was the specific site of female pleasure.....[and that] in the medical writing of his time, had asserted that the vagina had virtually no erotic functions at all ..... virtually the entire vagina could be operated on without the need of an anaesthetic.* [8] (Appignanesi, L. & Forrester, J. (1993) <u>Freud's Women.</u> London: Virago. p. 425)

All surgeons who operate on girls and women today *should* have accurate scientific information about the precise structure and function of the whole clitoris. They must be very careful not to cut into any part of the whole clitoris organ or its nerve endings accidentally. Ignorant, prejudiced and ill-educated surgeons can permanently interfere with a woman's sex orgasms.

All psycho-practitioners should also get some *accurate sex education* themselves - if they want to deserve their fees. *All* doctors and psycho-analysts should also be ethically *required* to study Dr. O'Connell's work - if they *really* want to help people and not harm them.

Don't **ever** go to a shrink who believes that the vagina is a woman's sexual organ - or who doesn't know how big the clitoris really is! Furthermore, it's not a bad idea to ask a female shrink whether she has regular and great orgasms herself – or to ask a male shrink whether he is *absolutely* sure his woman isn't faking.

People who don't know their own bodies and feelings are hardly likely to be **genuinely** able to help you manage yours. Actually, you probably don't need to ask. Sex-affirmative therapists have that orgasmic glow in their faces.

Understanding the clitoris's design could also help protect women's ability to have good sex. Colombo said: *"The only path that will lead us to an understanding of women's behaviour is the path of anatomy."* Freud also wrote that 'anatomy is destiny.'

But, of course, as I have shown, unconsciously or deliberately, (but definitely unfortunately for happy relationships between men and women) Freud got his female sexual anatomy completely WRONG. And most of his 'psychodynamic followers' today still practice these anatomical and psychological FALSEHOODS.

---

[8] Solomon's *Song of Songs* 4:16.

Here's some accurate anatomy:

> "According to O'Connell's [et al, 1998] descriptions, the cavernosal nerves [of the *whole* 5-inch clitoris] travel alongside the walls of the uterus, vagina, bladder and urethra. And although practically nothing is known about how operations for, say, incontinence or bladder cancer or hysterectomies affect sexual function, the positions of the nerves suggest that it could be at risk in lots of operations."

In the same article in the New Scientist, Dr. Amundsen said that, just as doctors routinely ask men who have had prostate surgery about their erections, they should always ask female patients who have had comparable operations about any changes in their sexual function.

Now the nerves' pathways are known, it should also be possible to modify at least some operations to reduce the risk of future sexual dysfunction which are surgically created by medical ignorance.

> *!* **Do not** allow any surgeon to operate on you - or any female person you care about - who cannot demonstrate, to your genuine satisfaction - that they know and understand the *orgasmic consequences* of any surgical procedure they are proposing.

> * I don't know of any exceptions.

> ? Have you asked your GP the question I suggested in the previous chapter yet? If you haven't, e-mail me with the reasons why not…

Chapter 5

The Best Sex Orgasms for Men and for Women

"Awake, O north wind; and come, thou south; blow upon my garden, that the spices thereof may flow out. Let my beloved come into his garden, and eat his pleasant fruits." [9]

The best sex orgasms for men and women have to involve **desire** – wanting to have them. And it is a truism that 'if you don't use it, you'll lose it.' Men usually get orgasms from sex, so they often want more of them. Women usually don't get orgasms from genital sexual intercourse, so they quite often 'go off' sex.

Although, as several men have told me, their wives (who after many years admitted that they have never had orgasms during sex) say they 'don't mind' - because she knows he 'has his needs' and wouldn't want him to 'stray' because of sexual frustration. (21ˢᵗ century professional wives!)

If I were a man being 'indulged' for my animal appetites by my *unusually* honest woman in this way, I know that *I* would feel inadequate, guilty, selfish, resentful, undesired and undesirable. I would also probably secretly lose my confidence around other men and other women until it pervades even the quality of my professional work and the rest of my life.

I'd definitely be off to a lapdancing club like thousands of my mates. But, I'll always be secretly dreaming of one lovely day coming across a

---

[9] Solomon's *Song of Songs*

woman who WANTS *me* sexually and who'll **come** for me because she LIKES it!

We are human animals, so obviously, if something is nice for us, we want to do it again. And again. And again. However, if something is *not* nice for us, we will find any excuse to avoid it. Again and again. Simple. 'My pre-menstrual tension'. My 'period' cramps. A headache. Too stressed at work. Too tired. You were late for dinner last night and I'm still upset about it. Whatever.

43% of women are now considered to be 'suffering from lack of desire'. It makes perfect sense. Why would any woman 'desire' sex if it is NOT nice for them? If they are **not** rewarded by that miraculous release of those brain-chemical medicinal highs which Nature provided for us with our orgasm reflex? IF sex leaves many women even *more* orgasm-starved and sexually frustrated?

Hundreds of women have, in confidence, said to me: **"No sex is almost always better than bad sex."** OF COURSE these women 'lack sexual desire'. Wouldn't you? Under similar conditions?

But, instead of providing people with accurate anatomical information and educating couples, what is the pharmaceutical industry wanting the doctors to do? For *43%* of the female adult population? Why, **sell them more pills** in order to get them to have more 'sexual desire'. The 'pink Viagra' no less.

Then these women's clitorises can get even more painfully erect and even more regularly 'frustrated' from *not* coming to orgasm with their men. And then they will buy even more pills for their depression, irritability and anxiety............

And/or, the alternative drug industry can sell stimulants like cocaine and heroin which mimic the brain's natural ability to produce those most intense thrills from orgasm and get people addicted to those *substitutes* for 'the real thing'......

Or these millions of women can get addicted to alcohol or food which they end up abusing in order to relieve their relational pain and sexual frustration……..

International research evidence is mounting that the brain regions implicated in addiction are similar in orgasm. Unlike harmful drugs, *orgasms build* respectful relationships, rather than *destroy* them. Furthermore orgasms are *FREE* and *HEALTHY!* Just think about this…………

Without some kind of reward no creature on earth will be interested in sex! (Or much else for that matter.) Lack of reward inevitably leads to lack of desire. Lack of desire inevitably leads to lack of motivation for non-orgasmic sex. Of course. It's obvious.

But, just you try getting some money for research that *won't* sell more pills. Only alleviate untold intimate human suffering. And make an enormous contribution to human happiness on a global scale. If you know how or where – PLEASE tell me.

Almost everybody knows that *the very best sexual orgasms* for a man comes from having his **penis** in somebody else's **mouth** who loves it competently and confidently until he comes. This is the way many guys like their orgasms best.

Most men orgasm happiest and fastest that way. 30 seconds to five minutes. **Same time** as most women need to come once – if competently LOVED. In 30 seconds to five minutes. So how can a man be 'diagnosed' as suffering from 'premature ejaculation'? Premature to what? Master's and Johnson's stopwatch?

I think only a man who orgasms in less than 30 seconds would meet the scientific and anatomical criteria for being 'premature'. But then he's probably very frustrated or very young and can probably come again and again…….. *So what's the problem?*

And similarly with what sexperts have labelled as 'delayed ejaculation'. Who is going to object to a man who just goes on and on with an erection for hours before he ejaculates? Only a bored and sexually dissatisfied woman. Whose time schedule should a body follow? The Sexperts ? Or Nature's? You choose.

And what about a woman who comes to orgasm within 30 seconds of a man touching her? Or speaking to her on the phone? Are we to also label *her* orgasm as 'premature'? Or focus on keeping her coming and coming and coming for as long as we both want?

I know of a woman who just couldn't stop orgasming, even after hours, until her LOVER had to put her in a cold bath! Personally I can keep coming for hours even after a LOVER has physically gone. If he's been any good that is. I *know* this ecstasy will (sadly) eventually stop. So no cold baths for me then thank you!

NOT everybody knows that the very best sex for a woman comes from having a **hand** love her **whole clitoris** until she comes and comes and comes and comes…. It's the most extremely intense delicious free thing on earth. And you can do it as often as you want to. (*No* pregnancy risk, only *infinitesimal* disease risk.)

Both men *and women* can easily come to orgasm heaven in these ways within 30 seconds to 4 or 5 minutes on average – *without any 'foreplay'*. That's how long most women and most men take to have an orgasm from masturbation! So, perhaps most 'foreplay' is merely a **consolation prize**. For not coming at all.

Of course, it only makes sense that men and women take about the same time to come *because* they have *the same sexual organ.* The clitoral phallus.

The BEST way to make a woman come has nothing to do with the penis. Yes, of course I know what the boys *believe*, but then, everybody used to believe that the earth was flat. Here's a little story for them:

Two men are walking across the San Francisco Bay Bridge. Towards the middle the one man says to the other: "*I need to take a leak.*" And the other guy says; "*Me too.*" Then the first guy says: "*Well, let's just do it right here.*"

So they both turn to face the bay, unzip their trousers and proceed with the operation. Pissing into the bay way below them that is. After a few seconds of this, the first man says to the other one: *"Wow, the water sure is cold down there!"* And the other one says: *"Yes, and deep!"*

Anyway, most women will, just like men, also only take 30 seconds to 5 minutes to come to orgasm with somebody else - IF their partner is a competent, confident and informed **hands-on** lover. However, I have seen in many cases that this natural orgasmic reflex may have been actually interfered with *if the woman has been using vibrators regularly to come to orgasm.*

Unfortunately, many sexperts, including some RELATE practitioners and other leaders of women's sexuality workshops recommend the use of *vibrators* for women to learn how to orgasm. Personally and professionally I think this is usually WRONG and HARMFUL – if not just simply commercially exploitative. I will explain why.

I generally advise women to stop using vibrators immediately and get with **natural** ways of coming. *For the men's information, only 1.7% of women use something for vaginal penetration during masturbation to orgasm.* The best-selling vibrators bought by women themselves are the **smallest** ones. Most lesbians don't use dildo's or vibrators either. Just THINK about that..........

Vibrators are BAD for women because it desensitises the clit-end - the little sticky out part of the 5 inch long whole clitoris. Then these ill-advised women, of course, end up needing **harder** and **faster** electrical stimulation to 'reach' for their mechanically induced clit-end orgasms.

If girls or women habituate to this completely *unnatural* way of coming, it logically becomes almost impossible for a man or another woman to make them come. I have seen vibrator ads claiming to be able to "GET AN ORGASM OUT OF A STONE"! Just go figure this one out.........
I don't think women are sexual stones.

Neither do I think that are vaginas *'hard wood'* - as dear confused Dr. Freud described them. Just think of the sexual frustration of his poor wife. It's totally obvious. You can just see it for yourself in photographs of her face.

No wonder our dear cocaine-addict Dr. Freud stopped sex at around 40 years of age. Until the day he died. Talk to me about 'genital immaturity' if you want to. **Genital senility** more like! (Perfectly preventable with truth medicine.)

The female clitoris knows perfectly well how to have NATURAL ecstatic orgasms by hand or by simple physical pressure - and many orgasms at that - without women being badly 'advised' by so-called 'sexperts' to electrically perform functional cliterodectomies on themselves!!!

The truth is that some 80% of men can't get their women to orgasm even *without* the women having been habituated to 'vibrators'. Just think for yourself how hard and impossible it must be for the men when the women have conditioned themselves to being so mechanically 'stimulated' to orgasm.

Just imagine all those thousands of well-meaning, but partially informed, 'new men' having to force themselves to try and be *faster* and *harder* than a battery-driven store-bought vibrator which is claimed to be able to get *"an orgasm out of a stone"!* Then listen carefully to all the words of the whole song by the Pointer **SISTERS** of *"I want man with a slow hand...."*

Anyway, the best way to give a man "a blow-job" (funny word isn't it?) is to put it gently into your mouth and love it with all your heart, mind and soul. Don't blow in it! This is because men feel themselves most in their penises. When you're loving a man's penis it's like you're loving the *whole of that man* and concentrating it all on his sexual organ. Treating him as your BELOVED.

The best way to give a woman an orgasm is to use your hands on her **whole** clitoris and love it with all your heart, mind and soul. This is because women feel themselves most in their clitorises. It's like you're loving *the whole of the woman* and concentrating it all on *her* sexual organ. Treating her as your BELOVED.

Because a penis is anatomically just the same thing as a clitoris, any man can easily understand how a woman feels and how she would like to be brought to orgasm. The only difference is that she actually has a greater part of her body involved - because of the two wings of her tulip-shaped clitoris extending into each of her thighs. If you measure it from end to end, the clitoris is some 19cm long because of its two wings (*crura*). This is almost twice the length of the penis. Make of that what you will.

Personally I think and feel that human beings **need to LOVE** even more than they need to be loved. All my research in Relationship Psychology, for which I got my second doctorate, shows this.

So, loving some body else sexually to orgasm is wonderful for all human beings. It's the very best glue for a loving relationship. The other chemical released then in our bodies is called oxytocsin. NATURAL ECSTASY. Free.

Now, we all know, or can imagine, how wonderful it is to *be* loved. So having someone give you the best sexual orgasm they have lovingly learned how, is **awesome** for all human beings - IF they want to do it.

Now the thing about heavenly orgasms is that you have to be able to **concentrate** your own whole body mind and soul into the *here-and-now* experience of your *own* sexual organ. You can't easily do this while also at the same time trying to do something to the other person.

Just visualise (or re-experience) what an erotically ambitious man has to do in conventional missionary position intercourse with a willing woman. He has to 'foreplay' – which most men's magazines acknowledge is 'boring' for most men. (Foreplay to *what* anyway? Nipple-or knee orgasms are still based in the clitoris, same as all thoughts are based in the brain!) Then the man has to position himself to be **hovering** over his woman's body, carrying all his own body weight on his forearms. (If they've been out for dinner, his belly is perhaps uncomfortably full and he might even have had a glass of wine - or more - to 'relax their inhibitions'.) He then, in addition, is expected to have a hard and strong erection for the whole time the 'genital sexual intercourse sex' goes on. (Bring on the Viagra or Cialis.) Since he's been a little boy he has anyway been pre-occupied with whether his penis is 'too small' or even 'too big' – this is the BIG moment of truth coming up! (Talk to me about 'performance-anxiety'.) Like most men he may be worrying about 'losing it' one way or another before he gets 'it' in. He is, of course, also expected to be passionately kissing her *at the same time* as whispering sweet nothings into her ear, while preferably also making deep and intense eye contact and telling her he LOVES her. Or kissing. (*Unless he's a Freudian who believes that "The mouth does 'not form part of the sexual apparatus because it is the entrance to the digestive tract.' Perversions are sexual activities e.g. kissing which either (a)* **extend** *in an anatomical sense, beyond the regions of the body that are designed for sexual union, or (b)* **linger** *over the intermediate relations to the sexual object which should normally be traversed rapidly on the path towards the final sexual aim." My emphasis.*)

When the man is **finally** joyously pumping his hard penis backwards and forwards into her vagina with his natural body thrusts you'd think he could just 'go with the flow' of Nature's ancient rhythms. But **NO.** *Now* he has to start concentrating his mind desperately on either 'cricket' or 'moving his chakra energy up to his third eye' - or his lover has to 'apply the squeeze technique'. If he's been reading the literature on "how to last longer" he must now SLAM the brakes on. This is in order to desperately *delay* his absolutely natural animal desire to ejaculate to orgasm (to 'last' beyond the 30 seconds to four minutes which is usually his body's natural anatomical time clock) until *she* comes to orgasm – which the sex manuals and his own bad previous experience usually tells him is going to take **much longer.** (Untrue – the clitoris is on the same biological clock as the penis. It's the same organ remember!)

So, some dear men are now putting an anaesthetic cream on their penis – so they feel *less* sensation in order to make themselves 'last longer'. Even if this means they feel less pleasure. So now we have chemically anaesthetised penises pumping away in biologically anaesthetised vaginas...... Anyway, if his beloved is like most normal women (80% of us), she won't orgasm anyway UNLESS he is at the same time *simultaneously* expertly and sensitively stimulating her clit-end. Her clit-end, which, of course, mostly responds to very gentle circular motions while his own natural body is wanting to BUCK backwards and forwards in strong linear motions – exactly the opposite. (Talk to me about patting your head and circling your other hand on your tummy at the same time!)

Optional extras, of course, include finding some extra hands on his body to throw in some expert breast and nipple action. *Is it any wonder that most men fantasise about having at least one other woman there to help out?*

Is it any wonder than so many men just collapse into disinterested and exhausted sleep immediately afterwards? During which they are not even allowed to snore? (Bring on the Nicotine patches!) No, the poor man is then furthermore expected to hold, kiss and cuddle her for quite some time. He now has to administer what I've heard called 'aftercare'. *While at the same* time he is desperately trying to fight and control his own almost overwhelming **biologically**-based physical and mental *compulsion* to just relax into a relieved and happy sleep – and have some peace!

So it might sometimes be better to take turns. Decide together who is going to be **The LOVER** and who is going to be **The BELOVED** for a particular **LOVE PRACTICE** sex session. A Love Practice Session needs a minimum of two hours. Why TWO HOURS if men and women can orgasm in five minutes or so?

Because 5 minutes can be all it takes to *start* having **MULTIPLE ORGASMS.** Which can go on for hours and hours – providing they have set the time aside. Both men and women deserve a LOT of time to enjoy their multiple orgasm trips thoroughly. Any really 'good trip' takes time.

Multiples for men? Yes. Lots. Even if they have suffered spinal injuries. Even if they don't or can't have erections. Ask Jack@multiples.com if you don't believe me. Tiresias was WRONG. But I fear ignorance, prejudice and lack of understanding of male psychophysiology is going to be even harder to overcome than explaining what the clitoris is and what to do with it.

So we'll just start with setting aside a regular weekly 2 hours period a week *in the morning* just after you've woken up. This is the best and minimum time needed for a good LOVE PRACTICE sex session with somebody being in charge - THE LOVER and somebody being pleasured – THE BELOVED.

You may switch these roles immediately afterwards, but often people are just too happily exhausted from riding the wave of their orgasmic ecstasy highs to do that particularly well.

I have found that it is much better to sleep first and *switch LOVER/BELOVED roles* later. Or the next day. Or next week. Then you can give and take when you are both (or all) refreshed, rested and energetic for more orgasmic ecstasy.

The LOVER is the person who takes the **initiative** and responsibility during a particular Love Practice sex session. The BELOVED is the person who receives and surrenders to the LOVER in that session.

Some people like being the BELOVED most of the time. Some people like being the LOVER most of the time. Some people like playing the BELOVED with some people and the LOVER with other people. Some people like switching these roles in a stable couple. They are sometimes called 'versatile'.

Anyway, apart from taking turns, the nice thing about Nature's fairness in this respect, is that you can 'tune in' to each other's pleasure in giving or taking at the same time. If it's done well, the initial separation between these two roles *merge.*

As one lovely LOVER put it between roars of orgasmic pleasure: *"Right now it's impossible to know where your body ends and mine begins. We've really become one."* And that was my experience too.

This kind of orgasmic sex is kind of **spiritual** – as you will find out for yourself, with a loving and erotically competent partner. This is not 'bonking sex' I'm describing here. This is MAKING **LOVE.** Extraordinary sex.

Giving love to someone else's bodysoul, doesn't mean that you're not 'getting' love yourself. *You **will** simply get out what you put in* – just the same as in all other areas of Life.

Indeed, giving with all your heart *usually* means you'll be getting to the same extent - even at the same time. But in a slightly different way. I haven't quite figured out how this works yet, but I know that it **does** work that way.

The reason **good orgasm giving is also at *the same time* good orgasm taking** is probably because modern physics shows us that people are not *really* separate at all levels. Our atoms and whatnot else kind of overlap or blend together anyway. Here is a picture of what we look like to physicists:

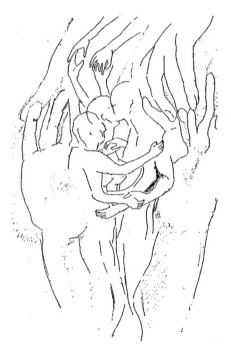

Human Quantum Entanglement

(You can check out for yourself the lovely original colour photographs in the magazine called the *New Scientist*, No. 2176, 6 March 1999.)

Blending, giving and taking, like in orgasmic sexual love, is probably the highest and best synchronization of our energetic *vibrations at all levels*. We could call it '**empathic attunement**' or '**visceral empathy**'.

It's like musicians 'tuning' their instruments to each other's so that they can play more beautiful music together. The better they are attuned, the fewer mistakes get made and the more fun everybody has. Like in a great Jazz jamming session.

Such empathic attunement is definitely physical – even cellular. The easiest way of attuning is through aligning your *breathing* to the BELOVED's breathing pattern and softly but audibly supporting the moans and sounds they are making with your own noises. Like harmonising music together.

Most women and many men think that orgasmic breathing is fast and increasingly rapid, building to a kind of climax by panting until you're quite out of breath. This is what people see in porn films. This is also what Meg Ryan demonstrated so hilariously 'faking it' in the restaurant scene of the film *"When Harry met Sally"*.

Real orgasmic breathing is **absolutely** different. There is no 'strain', no 'reaching' for orgasm, no effort *at all*. Nature *LIKES* having ecstatic orgasms. Through men and women. And your bodysoul knows exactly what to do – if you'll just trust its process.

Real multiple orgasmic breathing is difficult to describe, partly because we have ***never*** seen or heard it on a movie screen. I have never yet seen a full-body multiple ecstatic orgasm portrayed. Neither have many people ever heard or experienced it.

If you come to an Advanced Sexuality Workshop I'll demonstrate it for you while our rocking pelvises keep the beat. Then we could all experiment making the sound to get used to it. I also have an audiotape for sale to which you can listen and attune your own natural sounds and rhythms. (Please enquire.)

Personally, I discovered the **ECSTATIC ORGASMIC SOUND** *as just* *naturally* **COMING** *out of my body* when I started having multiple ecstatic orgasms only some few years ago. What happened was that I started the fullest, deepest breathing I had ever experienced. Just oxygen flowing completely out and in of my lungs – emptying out completely and filling up completely.

And then this cycle repeating and repeating for hours. Nothing to do with me. Everything to do with Nature doing its thing. This kind of ecstatic orgasmic breathing is actually *quite a slow process* – try it consciously yourself now….. Completely emptying your lungs of air and then completely letting them fill **naturally.**

The point is that in a multiple orgasmic ecstatic state, I feel no strain or conscious decision about my breathing at all. Nature is playing her own eternal music *through* the LOVERS. All we have to do is empty ourselves like flutes to the breathing of Life.

The first time I experienced this it just simply felt like the way *my body* liked to breathe in its most fulfilled and beautiful state. My heart, mind and soul just **surfs** along on this wind of Life. And my LOVER follows, carried effortlessly and orgasmically in the slipstream.

The first time, my breathing just kind of *exploded* into that pattern. I couldn't, and didn't want to, stop it. It was overwhelmingly joyous, flooding my every cell with life-giving oxygen and bringing sexual ecstasy to every vibrating fibre of my being.

And it went on and on and on. For hours. Easy. Completely full of air and then completely empty. Life flowing in and flowing out. Nothing to do with my conscious rational self. *Just **Nature** doing what she likes doing.* And us riding the waves of delight. At all levels simultaneously. Some psychologists have called this 'a peak experience'.

With this kind of breathing and coming all the time, I first vaguely heard a sound coming out of me like a long delicious AUHHH every time my breath came out. It didn't feel like *my* voice at all. It was more like the sound came from deep in my belly - giving music to the dancing of my clitoris and my snaking whole-body orgasms with my rhythmically rocking pelvis as the base drum beat.

The sound coming from my *comings* just got louder and louder until I was roaring like a magnificent lioness on an African Savannah. I felt as if I was *being* her – sharing her natural joyous animal ecstasy as if it never had to end. Yet, strangely I wasn't *thinking* at all. I was **gladly** lost in the best drug *TRIP* of my life.

And my LOVER was breathing with me and sounding with me. So I felt no embarrassment at my increasingly abandoned erotic noise. Just *his* excitement and ecstasy at me losing the boundaries of my earthbound ordinary self. Melting into glorious cosmic bliss – under his hands. (Yes, yes, eventually of course, the neighbours complained. But then I think they were just envious!)

It's like feeling from within your own body your sexual organ's movements permeating space and skin and sensing the sensations and rhythms the other person is experiencing. The best kind of orgasmic attunement is physical, mental, communicative, ethical, intelligent, imaginative and spiritual. All seven levels at the same time.

I know of several couples - really good practised and trained 'attuners' who actually have regular **physical** orgasms together at the same time in this way. And, for some people, this happens without even touching. (I've experienced this myself.) But, just like becoming a Wimbledon-winning doubles pair, it takes total commitment to training, regular practice and expert coaching.

Of course it's not *only* physical. **Attunement** also happens at an emotional level. It's feeling the other person's feelings, sensations, experiences and sounds vibrating and resonating outside, inside and around yourself.

When the LOVER hears and feels this, there is never any need to ask; "Did you come?" The natural orgasmic **roar** *cannot* be faked. Neither can our inner animals fail in recognising an animal truth.

Furthermore, men reporting back after even a white belt Advanced

Sexuality Workshop, frequently tell me that *"Her face was **glowing** the next day – all the tension and stress drained out of it. She looked years younger. She was more beautiful than I had ever seen her before."*

That is the look of an orgasmically sexually SATISFIED woman. Any man can recognise it. Unfortunately for everybody, we see it all too rarely.

When men experience their EROTIC POWER over a woman they love in this way they say things like: *"I felt her so open and vulnerable. I felt myself so protective and sexually potent."* I see the tears of joy and relief in the eyes of these men. I see **confident** and **compassionate** human males. I see MEN becoming more themselves in their personal lives and much more successful professionally. Lives change......

Which brings me to a **brain difference** between men and women in terms of words and images. Most women have between 14 and 16 key locations in *both halves* of their brains which are to do with communication – words, tone of voice changes, context and body signals.

Most men have only between 4 and 7 of these types of key brain locations to do with verbal communication. Their brains have evolved for spatial tasks to do with images, graphs, pictures and so on. **Therefore, erotically, guys are mostly hard-wired to images and pictures; whereas women are mostly hard-wired to words or sounds.**

That's why most men like to watch porn or *look* at pictures of naked women when they wank and why most women like to *read* erotic fiction like Black Lace novels or the Story of O (or *still* the best-selling of them all Barbara Cartland!) when *they* wank.

So if you want to sexually love a man, you need to give **visual stimulation** as well as *physical stimulation*. That's why most men prefer to **see** their cum on their partner's face or over their body when they orgasm. One couple told me that they like to do "the silver necklace" of his cum on her naked feet. To me, that sounds like an act of beautiful loving Goddess worship. Whatever you want to call it.

I'm told that most **gay guys don't swallow cum**. And *they* certainly should know what *men* like. Just research some porn movies and you'll see the same. Men also like their partners to dress up or down in various underwear or interesting costumes to stimulate them even more erotically through their eyes.

That's why so many men very hopefully buy their woman sexy lingerie at Christmas for example, and why so many women return these gifts when the shops open again. I think that those women just don't understand that it's only their LOVER's way of **please** asking them for more *visual* sexual excitement in bed. To increase the erotic ***intensity.***

If you love the guy, take the hint, wear the stuff - or something very similar (which actually fits) for your next LOVE PRACTICE sex session. It's a sure-fire way to help her attune to what he's implicitly asking for. And it shows him, in a way that he can **see** on your body, that you *care* about his orgasm heaven.

I'm sure that I don't have to spell out for anybody that the guy is then of course much more likely to give the other person what they want next time and to *care* about *their* orgasm heaven.

Dr. Freud kept complaining in his writing that he couldn't find out what women wanted. (Poor guy, he just couldn't believe own eyes or ears!) He wrote that the sexuality of women *"partly owing to the stunting effect of civilized conditions and partly owing to their conventional secretiveness and insincerity – is still veiled in an impenetrable obscurity." (p. 63)*

Freud was nominated for a Nobel Prize. But NOT for science. For *literature*! (There's no denying that he was a great story-teller.) Freud's female patients - and all psychoanalysts since following his psychoanalytic theories - especially the Lacanians - have accepted that *"**the elimination of cloridal [sic] sexuality is a necessary precondition for the development of femininity."** (p. 339)

This made most of the millions of women (80% of us) who cannot have orgasms from penile penetration alone because we are *anatomically normal,* in Freud's own words: 'obstinate', 'secretive', 'sexually crippled', 'immature', 'emotional' and 'insincere'. WOW!!!! Is this an understanding, non-judgemental empathetic sex doctor or what? No wonder he rarely 'cured' anybody. He just *psychoanalysed* them. It's not the same thing at all.

Dr. Fraud, you really should have actually read your German textbooks properly when you were a student in medical school. Let me tell you what all those Viennese ladies were doing making 'strange' noises and arching their backs so 'hysterically' while they were lying on the couch in your consulting room. When you were *talking* to them about **sex**. They were **COMING!**

What women want sexually is simple. **Women want orgasms. From their sexual organs. Their clitorises. Same heavenly orgasms as men want.** Nature decreed that every *body* has a phallus. Argue with NATURE if you want to, not with me. I'm only the messenger.

But I digress. What women like a lot for sex orgasms are *sounds and words* – stimulation for their ears. Or those parts of their brain which are concerned with language. (*And, of course, LOVERS who know their anatomy.*)

Almost all people in the world like to be told that they are loved, but you have to mean it sincerely when you say it to a BELOVED. If you can't do this *sincerely,* then you can describe and tell them that you **love** their eyes, breasts, bottoms, legs, nipples, skin, cocks, touch, neck, knees, hair – whatever truly turns *you* on as their LOVER…..

A darling lover of mine pulls on my pubic hairs, sexually arousing all the erotically super- sensitive flesh beneath with these movements of his loving hands. I had never felt my **erotic fur** so **INTENSELY** as the first time when he breathily whispered: "*I can feel all your little hairs getting excited.*"

Now I can hardly ever be conscious of them - in going to the toilet, in showering or dressing - without hearing his low and sensuous voice commenting on my genital hairs and erotically turning me on to him again and again and again. (*I'd do just about anything for **him**… of course.*)

Personally, I always suspect men who want *shaven pussies* of harbouring paedophiliac tendencies and lacking sensory empathy. What truly sensual grown-up woman wants all that horrible itching constantly between her legs? What genuinely sensual man wants beard-rash on his face?

However, as the Kama Sutra so quaintly puts it: *"But after all, these things being done secretly and the mind of the man being fickle, how can it be known what any person will do at any particular time and for any particular purpose."*

A Crash Course in Sex Talk:

• GREEN LIGHT: Flirting is all about implicit sex talk or knowingly 'innocent' talk using words and images with sexual references, *double entendres* in conversation, flattering and arousing compliments or self-references, nicknames, for example, for sexual parts and sexually interesting jokes. This is often funny or humorous and arousing.

• AMBER LIGHT: "Explicit Porn talk" Using sexual words and phrases which are usually forbidden on TV (except sometimes). This kind of sex talk is usually more serious and an area which is highly sexually arousing and can lead to great orgasms for both people.

• RED LIGHT: 'Bad' sexual talk; When the names of sexual organs or the acts of sex are used to insult, humiliate or hurt the other person. In my opinion this is best avoided because it is often linked to damaging and hurtful other aspects of the relationship – or abusive sexual behaviour.

•*There is one exception:* This is erotic discovery. Red light sex talk is a great opportunity for role-play exploration and erotic discovery IF the rest of the relationship is good and not damaging to either partner. This is the danger zone. Don't go there if you haven't both agreed it's a harmless turn-on or a favourite orgasm **detonator**.

So, just the same as a woman has to empathically imagine what her man wants to **see,** a man has to empathically imagine what his woman wants to **hear** for her best ecstatic sex heaven, and give it to her as best he can – or go and learn how to…..

That is, *if* he cares about her and if he wants her to *want to* care more about his orgasm heaven. ***It's the natural law of increasing returns.*** Smart move. Smart movers.

! There are, of course, women who prefer to look and guys who prefer to listen. I think the very best sex orgasms come from pleasing *all* the senses: touch, taste, hearing, seeing, smelling, tasting and intuition – excluding only those which can interfere with your BELOVED'S concentration. **This is called the *Ars Erotica* or the Art of Sensuality.**

* There are almost always exceptions. But you certainly can't expect anybody else to know your personal individual sexy turn-on buttons unless you first find them out for yourself. This should be everybody's *first* priority. It's really not difficult. What makes **you** come most *intensely?*

? SPOT THE ERRORS EXERCISE: Here follows an extract from a book called ***"Understanding Sex for Medical Doctors"*** published by the **British Medical Association** (Low & Smith, 2001, p. 7). "Think about it………."

THE FEMALE SEX ORGANS

The female organs are more complicated than the male sex organs. Internally, in the lower abdomen, sits the uterus or womb, the fallopian tubes and the left and right ovaries. The lower end of the uterus forms the cervix, which juts into the top end of the vagina. The vagina opens out into the external organs, which include the urethra, the clitoris and the vulva.

The Clitoris

The clitoris is in many ways a tiny penis. It has the same basic structure of the three tubes along its length and, when a woman is aroused, it also swells and becomes stiff. It is extremely sensitive to touch, being packed with nerve endings, and although women become sexually aroused by stimulation of the clitoris, movements that are too heavy and clumsy can be painful.

Chapter 6

How best to make a man come

Sensual sucking involves a complete absorption of the attention and leads either to sleep or even a motor reaction in the nature of an orgasm.[10] [Footnote added by Freud in 1920] *In 1919, a Dr. Galant published, under the title of "Das Lutcherli", the confession of a grown-up girl who had never given up this infantile sexual activity and who represents the satisfaction to be gained from sucking as something completely analogous to sexual satisfaction, particularly when this is obtained from a lover's kiss: Not every kiss is equal to a "Lutcherli" – no, no, not by any means! It is impossible to describe what a lovely feeling goes through your whole body when you suck; you are right away from this world. You are absolutely satisfied, and happy beyond desire. It is a wonderful feeling; you long for nothing but peace – uninterrupted peace. It is just unspeakably lovely: you feel no pain and no sorrow, and ah! you are carried into another world."*[11] (p. 97)

The best book I've found so far on how best to make a man come is written mostly by a gay man. Well, that's straight from the horse's mouth so to speak! Dan Anderson was kind enough to share with the rest of us his expertise based on many years of personal and varied experiences in doing and receiving blow-jobs - and other ways of sexually pleasing men.

Although I personally find his style of writing *not* to my liking, he has some excellent information to share. It is the book I would recommend to **anybody** wishing to give men heavenly orgasms. Of course you will blend with your own individual erotic style and adapt it to yourself as the unique sexual person *you* are.

---

[10] Freud, S. (1977) On Sexuality: Three essays on the theory of sexuality and other works. Trans. Strachey. Compiled and edited by Angela Richards. London: The Pelican Freud Library, Volume 7, p. 97.
[11] Ibid

Here I'm just going to focus on **"the one thing that most men seem willing to die for"** – **a good blow-job.** Loving a man's penis to heavenly orgasm involves using your mouth, your tongue and your hands competently. Supplemented by your heart, your mind and your soul. Of course.

Starting with his flaccid cock, you can put your BELOVED's penis all in your mouth gently and lovingly suck and lick it until he becomes erect. Don't be disappointed if he doesn't get hard. The wonderful **sensation bath** you're giving his nervous system with your intense concentration will be awesome for him. Do it for *at least* ten minutes anyway. Detach from 'results'.

It helps to tell your BELOVED beforehand that this is what you are going to do and for how long - whether or not he gets an erection. This takes the 'performance pressure' off him. He can just lie back and **luxuriate** in enjoying your erotic ATTENTION to his body.

Naturally, as I've explained before, if you're also wearing *his* favourite sexy costume, it's going to be even better for both of you. Depends on what **he** likes best. (As long as you yourself are not desperately uncomfortable of course.)

You **need** to be comfortable *for all the time* you have specified kneeling on pillows - or whatever - so that you can happily and in a relaxed way take control of the sexual initiative by erotically tuning into his breathing, his body sensations and your own physical and emotional responses. This can be ***amazing***!

Just make sure your sexiest stimulus – *for him* - is in his line of vision so that he can **look** as much as he wants to. For yourself, just realize that you have the whole of that man concentrated in that penis (your BELOVED'S 'manhood') with nerve-endings reverberating pleasure right throughout his body, mind and soul.

The goal is to get *every cell of your bodies* vibrating together with sexual excitement and orgasmic pleasure. You'll be **listening** for sexy changes in his breathing, moaning sounds of pleasure received, exclamations of delight or surprise. You'll **know** when the Natural Orgasmic Miracle starts happening.

It helps if you can also keep your own mind concentrating on all the reasons why you love this man. For example, what you liked most about him when you first met, the wonderful orgasms he has given you, the best sexual fantasy you've ever shared with him. (You'll know of other ways too.)

Concentrate your mind for those uninterrupted ten minutes (or however long the CD lasts) entirely on your BELOVED. Remind yourself why you admire and how you respect him. Think of all the nice things he has ever done for you. Think of how much he deserves a **heaven break** from all the stresses and strains of his ordinary life.

This is your chance to '*love him better*'. The profound HEALING power of ecstatic orgasmic sex is vastly underrated. Personally I think most men are **love-starved** and most women are **orgasm-starved.** I also think these are interrelated with each other. This could change if we wanted it to..........

My own LOVERS have certainly *healed* the physical, emotional and spiritual wounds Life has dealt me in so many delightful, yet lasting, ways. I am grateful to you all. I also appreciate your appreciation for what healing you have taken from me. For better and worse, it has made me into *the ecstatic multiply orgasmic woman* I EN-JOY being today.

It **helps** most women, with their brains' hunger for words and sounds, to have some music playing – or be hearing the sounds of the ocean or a thunderstorm - to listen to while they are being the LOVER. It also helps to set the natural rhythms and help *him* to relax into being your BELOVED. Many guys don't know how women just **adore** hearing the ragged changes in your breathing when you get really aroused. So, please don't hold back. We like it!

The whole LOVE PRACTICE sex session should be like a good piece of music itself with a beginning, a middle and an end. All of a piece - yet with different sections flowing into each other just like a fine song.

Yes, it's like singing a beautiful love song with your mouth and hand to your BELOVED. Try *humming* this song with your man's penis in your mouth.......

Erotically loving a man's penis in this way should obviously **not** be boring - just the same movement over and over again. Build in variety, changes of pace, changes of rhythm. Changes in type of stimulation or changes of temperature can be particularly exciting. For example, a LOVER'S mouth warmed from hot tea or chilled with the coolness of an ice-cube can create delicious intensely contrasting sensations for him - if he can get to like it.

Make a beautiful artistic five-course Michelin rated Gourmet Sensual Menu for him from the storehouse of your memories of him. Add your own creativity and inventiveness. Just for this little eternity you can dream whatever erotic fantasy you want - as long as you **create poetry in motion with your mouth and hands.**

Neither should you have jerky passages or clumsy interruptions which disturb the melody of his sexual enjoyment. *You are stroking one of Nature's most frightened and stressed-out animals.* Whatever macho posturing they sometimes do elsewhere.

This unique man is trusting **you** to take control of his whole nervous system. Repay that trust with consideration of what everything you do, and how you do it, feels like your BELOVED from the *inside* of him.

Hold his penis at the base where it goes into his body with your one hand like a fleshy cock ring to get a good, firm trustworthy reliable grip on it - but not too hard. This encourages the blood to that area and stimulates an erection - if his body feels like having one. It also gives you an anchor for your work of love.

It also gives him the feeling that your mouth is very deep and tight because, in this holding pattern, with your hand clasped around his penis, it feels like an extension of your mouth. **Just imagining this will help.**

It also helps *you* because it is then less likely that he will thrust too deep, too violently into your mouth and accidentally stimulate your gag reflex. This is when there is a fleeting feeling of wanting to throw up. This needs to be avoided since it obviously breaks your BELOVED's **erotic trance** – the blissful extended ecstatic state of altered consciousness which is sexually '*BEING IN THE ZONE*'. Even better than in golf.

It's best to relax the muscles in your jaw or neck. That's why it's so important that you, as the LOVER, should be physically comfortable. It also helps if you breathe through your nose. It may take some training and expert love coaching before you can do the job *competently* and confidently. But it can be done **beautifully**.

If you hold your tongue up across your epiglottis at the back of your throat, he can enjoy the feeling of pushing against it with every in-stroke. Your hand at the base of his penis should also *make you feel more secure* about not gagging, because that way you can guard against him going in too far or too deep unexpectedly.

Most men *love* a woman taking control of them sexually. Every healthy body likes having a turn at being THE BELOVED. That's why *dominatrixes* are so well paid and so popular with so many men in this culture. Naturally dominatrix rarely, if ever, do 'sexual intercourse' with their clients. These sex and fantasy workers don't have to! They are the professional LOVERS of male bodies. And their customers just keep on coming. And coming.

It's evidently NOT necessary to have conventional penis-in-vagina genital intercourse in order to bring a man to ecstatic sexual bliss. For example, many men *and women* can come to orgasm from a deliciously applied consensual, competent and desired sensual spanking alone. This can be an end in itself.

However, to do Expert Erotic Spanking needs a lot of proper training and coaching. (It is NEVER to be confused with violence!) If done well, a loving spanking brings all the blood's extra sensual sensitivity to the lower sexual body regions and maximises the natural aphrodisiac chemicals of Power Sexplay. You get visual *evidence* of your sexual impact on your lover. A reddened bum also reminds our erotic DNA under-consciousness of the archetype of our gloriously coloured ape ancestors' bottoms......

But you don't have to be a professionally mentored Sex Worker in order to learn many erotic skills competently and become the most wonderful and unforgettable LOVER your man has ever had.

Remember that your BELOVED may also be *very nervous* (even if he doesn't know how to show it) because he may never have had such complete sexual attention before. Tell him that you are going to give him an **ATTENTION BATH.** You need to reassure him that you **want** to love him in this way and that you are not going to hurt him, rush him or make demands on him for *his* time together in orgasmic ecstasy heaven with you.

Just remember that most men are not necessarily good about telling women what they want because of the way their brains are made. It's hard enough for men to find out what they're feeling *themselves* in the first place.

And too many men have **never** had their penises s l o w l y **gentled** all the way to and from the peaks of ecstasy by a competent and confident LOVER. And even fewer men have been erotically seduced by their lovers into having multiple orgasms which go on and on and on...... But let's start by getting him used to being the BELOVED.

As I've explained, women are neurologically hardwired to be better communicators with words than most men. Therefore, you can help him to find out what *his* sexual organ likes in terms of ecstasy.

Your BELOVED himself, may have *no idea.* He **needs** your help. But always remember that erotic feelings are often so wonderfully powerful that they simply cannot be put into words. This is where your natural woman's intuition comes into its own.

I'm sure you've seen guys wanking! And if you're a woman yourself you must have experienced the similar hard and fast, *erratic* attack some guys make on your clitend. OUCH! So, at first, your BELOVED may need **your skilful help** to get over the unfamiliarity of genuine sexual pleasure exploration into ecstasy.

Men are generally *love starved*. That's why one of the most popular requests from them to professional sex workers is **GFE**. (Girl friend experience.) There are many men out there willing to pay good money for some woman who will just be NICE to them.

Doesn't that rip some compassion out of you? Doesn't that tell you that something has gone horribly wrong as result of the Sex Wars? Doesn't that make you *want* to contribute to '**a peace process for the gender wars**'? (That's my secret name for the work I am doing now.)

The basic blow-job movement is with your lips over your BELOVED'S penis in a rhythmic forwards and backwards motion. (You need to make your mouth as taut - tight - as your hand ringed around the base of the penis.) This is like the basic bass line or drum beat of the music. You **must** be careful with your teeth. You do not want to *shock* his system with *unexpected* **bad pain** in the middle of a sex session.

Some sexperts advise LOVERS to cover your teeth with your lips, but I think that looks funny and it isn't that comfortable for a long time. Also, a guy *likes the look* of his penis going in and out of the LOVER'S mouth and they like *seeing* your **lips** while you do it. That's why guys find a **woman's mouth** so erotic – whatever she's doing with it - like putting on lipstick in public after a meal.

I've also found that if you use your teeth very very gently, it provides additional stimulus variety and that men like it very much for its dangerous kind of **intensity**. They just want to be *sure* that you won't hurt them. Good pain must feel GOOD.

A BELOVED's penis is *extremely* sensitive to pain - just like a woman's clitoris. That figures, because, unlike the vagina, but just like the clitoris, the penis is extremely sensitive to **pleasure**.

Treat your BELOVED'S sexual organ in the same way as you would like him to handle yours. Remember, it's the **same** physical organ. Modelling behaviour - showing by example - is the fastest way of teaching many skills easily and quickly. And anyway most men learn best from *spatial* instruction.

As the BELOVED here learns to tolerate and enjoy all the erotic sensations of his body, he is also *at the same time* learning in a subconscious way, from **inside** himself, what you can feel when he makes love to you in a similarly dedicated way. (You could also research 'mirror-neurons' on the net if you're interested.)

Most deliciously sensitive in a man is a point on the ridge just under the top part - that is the part of his penis which is furthest from your BELOVED's face. So be sure to tease a lot and use your tongue here to bring on an erection or an orgasm if and when you're both ready for it.

You can roll you tongue into a kind of tube; use the flat part to stroke the shaft of the penis; lick, suck and flick it around. When he starts moaning or breathing very harshly, *keep your stroke going just the way you're doing it.*

The moaning means: "*Yes, more of the same please*". So **don't** suddenly change at that moment. It's your LOVER'S positive feedback to you that you're reaching his erotic sex buttons. Keep playing those buttons which make the most delicious music.

A great variation, once you've discovered his most *extreme* erotic reaction is to tease him a little by repeatedly approaching and withdrawing from this point. But please do it **elegantly** – and only for as long as you promised him - before you release him to have the most ecstatic orgasm of his life!

Men love having their balls and scrotum slowly played *with at the same time as having the penis inside your mouth.* (Remember that this scrotal flesh is **anatomically** the same as your outer vaginal lips – your labia. You know what feels best there.)

Ball and scrotum sexplay is a job for your other hand. Tickle, sensually stimulate, pull softly, whip lightly with your hair, stroke, knead, use feathers, fur, leather, silk. Whatever variations you can think of to entertain your BELOVED's entire nervous system. Bring him within *your erotic power.*

There's a beautiful scene by the fridge in the movie 9¹/₂ weeks. Watch it on DVD for an example of seeing an *Erotic Master* at work in creating intensely contrasting sensations in his BELOVED. Watch how he **concentrates** on her sensual reactions. See how he, as her LOVER, **DELIGHTS** in them.

Create your own variations to increase and develop the intensity of your erotic encounters when you're the LOVER. Aim to make *every* time you make love an event your BELOVED will never **ever** forget. Erotic intensity does not come from speed. It comes from intense ATTENTION – filling every moment with multiple sensations so that a minute feels like an eternity.

All healthy human creatures like *intensity*. Intensity makes us feel most fully ALIVE. Intensity comes from *strongly contrasting sensations*. Lack of intensity in orgasmic sexplay leads to boredom and the widespread phenomenon of sexless or sex-starved marriages.

If that's the way you want to live your erotic life, it's OK by me. However, if you don't, you can explore – forever - how to feel *more fully alive in sex* than any other activity on earth I can think of.

Which brings me to the good and ethical uses of erotic power. Kissinger is claimed to have said that: *"Power is the greatest aphrodisiac."* Power is accurately defined by Chambers dictionary as *"the ability to do anything – physical, mental, spiritual, legal, capacity for producing an effect"*.

POWER IS SEXY. And the erotic power of producing the *effect* of massively marvellous orgasms at physical, mental, spiritual, natural chemical and legal levels in a consenting partner is........(words failed me!)

It's better not to separate your BELOVED's two balls. **Remember he is trusting you to take good care of his most vulnerable body parts**. Handle them like the 'family jewels' they are. *Don't* make sudden moves. Gradually increase your pace or kind of stimulus or pressure in small increments only. So that you can follow and respond to his body signals immediately to do more or less or whatever.

With practice, you will soon learn to 'read' your BELOVED erotically. Then it all gets beautiful *and easy*. Just like an acclaimed concert pianist's performance is the end result of **years** of daily keyboard practice. However, it *looks* like they're doing the whole thing effortlessly and elegantly - when they are on the stage.

With the LOVER'S hand which is not holding his penis like a cock-ring around the base of the shaft, you can also *play with your fingers around his anus*. Most men **love** this, but they're afraid to ask in case somebody calls them 'homosexual' – whatever that means when it's at home.

I have observed that most healthy human beings will seek affection and/or sex orgasms wherever they are. When they are confined to same sex establishments such as boarding schools, oil rigs, prisons they just keep on doing it. Whatever their *preferences* when outside.

It's just NATURAL. Sexual play with others of the same gender is widespread and common with animals and insects of all kinds – including penguins, whales, baboons, gulls. Even fruitflies. In captive rhesus monkeys, males sometimes *prefer* to have anal sex with each other rather than to copulate with females.

It's **obvious** these creatures are having all kinds of *intense* sexual fun with each other. Fun is here defined as something you want to do again – and again – and again.

I make no moral judgement about the sexual behaviour of these *animals* and refuse to speculate on whether or not this kind of sexplay is 'caused' by genetic or social factors.

I must say though that I find it *really* hard to believe that those gay fruitflies all had 'dominant' mothers and 'weak' fathers as Dr. Freud would want us to believe is true about human beings!

However, now, on the basis of scientific facts, I think and feel that sexual bio-diversity among humans is as important as any other kind of bio-diversity and that this variety of sexual pleasuring on the planet should be preserved and valued. They might have much to teach the rest of us about all the sexual pleasures which are *not* to do with baby-making or pretend-baby-making. (Otherwise known as ***coitocentrism).***

So why love your man's anus? Only because Nature put millions of pleasure-sensitive nerve-endings there. So it's only NATURAL that **we all** want to feel and give as much pleasure there as we can tolerate. (Surely, Nature didn't do this rich and complex nerve-arrangement in our arseholes *only* for the admittedly sensual pleasures of shitting?)

If your BELOVED can tolerate the pleasure of your fingers playing around his crinkly rosebud starfish and begins to obviously enjoy it, experiment with slipping your little finger slightly inside. Go slowly and very gently. If you need to use lubricant it's OK of course, but saliva and the anus' natural juices are usually sufficient and better.

There's a sphincter in you BELOVED's anus which will have to stretch to let you in to love him over any shame he might have been taught to feel in there. Whisper that you are loving *all of him. Every part of his body is OK with you.* (Don't do this, if you cannot be sincere!)

If your BELOVED lets more of your finger in – or two longer fingers – find his G-spot equivalent. It has the same texture as yours. This wonderful site of multiple male orgasmic pleasure is also known as '**the black pearl**'. This is the prostrate gland - which lies *about* two or three inches inside his anus near the top part – the part nearest his heart. Massage it gently with a circular motion, increasing the pressure of your fingerpads, and just see what happens…

Just like when a woman first has to get used to how unexpectedly orgasmic and long-lasting her extreme orgasmic sexual pleasure can be, most men are also not used to experiencing such ecstatic orgasmic intensity. So, the first impulse is to think you're going to pee.

This feeling will pass. It's an erotic threshold which, as your BELOVED's tolerance for orgasmic ecstasy grows, will get easier and easier to cross without any accident. If you do this very s l o w l y and he can tolerate the natural orgasmic waves coming through his whole body, it is *not impossible* that the multiply orgasmic SOUND will naturally start coming out of your BELOVED.

If a LOVER already has personal experience and confidence in this amazing human sexual phenomenon, she'll know what to listen for and how to support it growing louder and louder until the BELOVED is ecstatically ROARING.

Just the way I described it earlier. Then you two can stay there in **heavenly orgasmic bliss** on the other side of ordinary consciousness for whatever time you both have agreed. As you *will discover*, erections and ejaculation *naturally* become **irrelevant.** Most men remember orgasming well before they discovered ejaculation when they were boys. That natural orgasmic reflex is still there. The body remembers. Our DNA *knows.*

Male multiple orgasms have much more to do with **UNLEARNING** our *anti-ecstatic social conditioning* than learning *yet* more artificial techniques of 'ejaculation control' which interfere with our natural uncontrolled orgasmic ecstatic capacity.

But please don't be disappointed with only one male orgasm. It takes some LOVE SKILLS COACHING and DEDICATED LOVE PRACTICE to get beyond it. First the human male has to be *eroticised.* And that is what the LOVER is starting to do with her regular attention baths. It's not a quick result we're looking for, but starting up an ecstatic **process** which can continue to get better and better for as long as he lives.

It is necessary to keep the nails of those fingers you're using for the erotic prostrate massage very clean and rather short. Even if they like long nails, good female LOVERS have shorter fingernails on two fingers of one hand - or they put little pads of cotton wool around their nails inside a rubber glove.

Ensure that there are **no rough edges** to your skin which can hurt the delicate membranes of your BELOVED'S anus. *Never* do this if you have cuts or infections on the skin of your hands. (This is easy to test by washing your hands in some lemon juice water first.)

Of course, if your BELOVED doesn't like it, you must NOT force it or make him in any way feel bad about it. Another time when he is again in the role of The BELOVED, he might feel more relaxed and experimental - and let you try it again.

He will *certainly* be giving you clear feedback about this. Just follow his non-verbal body signals and adjust your actions accordingly. And all this time you are also teaching him how to work your own G-spot to orgasm in a way that he just can't help learning subconsciously!

One woman, after a Love Coaching session, wrote this: "*I can tell you this much: there's a place inside a man's anus that, when stimulated expertly, makes him shudder with pleasure, come like a fountain, and buy his wife jewellery. And I've been there.*"

If you think orgasmic sex for a man can't get any better than this, I have to disappoint you. Finally, there's **the million-dollar point** – an erotic dynamite spot about halfway between the base of the penis (under the balls) and his anus. *The perineum.*

Start gently and erotically massaging the middle of this - his most sensitive perineal flesh - until you can feel him naturally getting into the rhythm of your fingers. Watch for, or encourage, his pelvis rocking forwards and backwards. Support his natural full body orgasmic breathing pattern any way you find how. You're using the pads of your two fingers in a circular rhythm of course, perhaps while continuing to play your pinky in his arsehole.

When *you give him permission to come – or* 'Mistress-fully' **order** *him to come* and your BELOVED starts ejaculating, press quite firmly on this spot - but not too hard. (Press, don't poke!)

This will prolong and intensify his orgasm and he might just pass out from natural ECSTASY. Don't be surprised if he starts having multiples. Just support his natural orgasmic sounds with your own. He'll be expecting to stop after one orgasm. Nature allows him as many as he can tolerate.

Remember that the orgasmic erotic breathing rhythm is *natural*. There is nothing to learn. Nature knows how. **Let him rest and sleep**. Cover him up with something warm and soft. But stay close to him physically until he has quite come down.

To help him do this, you may want to gently stroke his hair or his face, complimenting him on how well he was *THE BELOVED to your LOVER*. Then reassure him that's there's **nothing expected from him now** except to fully enjoy the very last drop of his exquisite erotic sensations as they begin to fade away.

! If you have *any doubt whatsoever* about hygiene or the smoothness of your skin, wear a disposable sensitive surgical rubber glove on the hand you use for his anus. You can buy these cheaply in packs from any chemist.

* There are almost always exceptions. But if your BELOVED lets you play the whole erotic concerto for him, do let me know if he liked it...

? We learn at home or at school how to brush our teeth. Don't you think we should all be taught how to sexually pleasure other human beings - if and when we feel like doing it?

Chapter 7

How best to make a woman come

"I felt the outflicking of her tongue ere it reached me, touched my lovelips. I wanted not to moan. I must not moan. Thumbs parted my love lips and sought my clitoris, my button, my ariser. The tongue tip swirled. It knew its cunning. Ah! she was good. Starshells burst in my belly. I whimpered, ground my hips. Her tongue would not reach into me. I wanted it. Did I cry out? On the brink of my salty spray, my spilling, I tremored in a cloud of delight. 'There is nothing to say. It's all in the doing.' [12]

I don't have one best book on how to make a woman come. In my opinion, both Lou Paget's *"How to give her Absolute Pleasure"* and Steve and Vera Bodansky's *"Extended Massive Orgasm"* have some useful and some not-so-useful (and some inaccurate) information. You should check them out and test what these authors say for yourself.

Although Freud wrote that cunnilingus and anilingus was 'disgusting', because it did not lead to the rapid union of the organs designed for making babies, people have always been doing it for ecstatic sexual orgasms. And no doubt will continue doing it.......

For very detailed instructions to perform cunnilingus on the *clit-end* **only** you could read the book called *'Satisfaction'* which Kim Cattrall of *"Sex and the City"* wrote with her sex therapist husband. (They're divorced now. No wonder.)

Cunnilingus is very pleasant and, if well done, can certainly lead to orgasm for women. Just as often and just as fast as a man can orgasm from having *only the helmet of his penis* licked. That's the anatomical equivalent of the little clit-end. Nice, but partial.

---

[12] Beatrice: Anon

Mind you, even partial can be fantastic! Here's a relevant piece from the famous Hindu Kama Sutra:

"Some women of the harem, when they are amorous, do the acts of the mouth on the yonis [they think a woman's sexual organ is the vagina!] of one another, and some men do the same thing with women. The way of doing this (i.e. of kissing the yoni) should be known from kissing the mouth.[?!] When a man and a woman lies down in an inverted order, i.e. with the head of he one towards the feet of the other and carry on this congress, it is called the 'congress of the crow'.

For the sake of such things courtesans abandon men possessed of good qualities, liberal and clever, and become attached to low persons, such as slaves and elephant drivers."

[I'm not agreeing with their value system that some people are 'lower' than others, but I see how an expert cunnilinguist could completely disrupt the usual *status quo!* If you remember that 'the West' is **Indo-European**, the following warning to men of good standing NOT to do cunnilingus, also makes sense:]

"The Aupraishtaka, or mouth congress, should never be done by a learned Brahman, by a minister that carries on the business of the state, or by a man of good reputation, because though the practice is allowed by the Shastra's [religious law], there is no reason why it should be carried on, and need only be practised in certain cases."

The Kama Sutra doesn't say in *which* cases. Perhaps they are alluding to the fact that even a man 'of good reputation' might just 'lower' himself to do 'mouth congress' in such cases where his wife is in danger of running off with 'a slave' or an 'elephant driver' who actually *LIKES* doing cunnilingus!

Research reported at the time of revising this, February 2003, claims that a larger and larger percentage of women are going outside of marriage for sexual satisfaction. Think about that.........

What I am going to tell you about now is NOT in the Kama Sutra – nor anywhere else - as far as I know. To me, all those hundreds of detailed intercourse positions the assumed author, Vatsyayana, describes *trying so hard* to get the vagina to be a sexual organ – which it is not - merely seems to be the vain and fruitless efforts of desperately confused men who just can't figure out how to sexually satisfy their women.

No wonder that there is so much copy in that ancient text devoted to dealing with 'lover's quarrels'! Now contrast that with what Matteo Colombo, who knew only about a *little* part of the clitoris said: *"As the treatment advanced, so to does the will of the patient become further ensnared; her readiness and obedience appear to have neither measure nor limit."*

In the meantime, here we go with describing the sexual technique which I figured out on the basis of **accurate** anatomical information about the female sexual organ and psychophysiology. It has been tested by many other real 21st century couples and has been found the best and most reliable position of all for ecstatic female orgasms.

In *this* LOVE PRACTICE Sex Session, **you** are The LOVER *taking control of her nervous system.* She is The BELOVED allowing you to take her on a journey to the best ecstatic orgasm heaven she's ever experienced.

Most healthy women just *love* losing erotic control to a competent sexually confident LOVER. Just like with men, the tougher and stronger and more successful the female BELOVED is, the more she usually erotically **craves** *giving over* for a little eternity to someone else's initiative – a LOVER.

Someone who knows what they're doing with her body and her mind. **It's a sure-fire stress and pain reliever *and* also supports her immune system. Apart from which it makes her happy……..**

Almost all adult women in our culture were first *eroticised* as girls by someone's hands. **Hands woke us up to our sensuality** with other people. Ask any honest woman. We *like* being fingered. For as long as you enjoy it - or until your arms drop off.

For a woman in The BELOVED role, **your *hands* are your sexual organs**. Men tend to focus erotically on the mouth. Women tend to focus erotically on your hands. So your hands better be clean, skill-full and talented!

A woman is like a waiting guitar for your hands to play music with her whole clitoris – not just plucking one or two strings. So guys who know how to stroke animals, or who play music, or use their hands competently and skilfully in other ways, often make the very Best LOVERS. It's men *spatial talent again...*

No matter what the men physically look like. As long as they are *clean*. Women are less fussed about looks than men. **Women are fussed about words and sounds**. These are usually their favourite turn-on buttons. So, don't let the erotic airways be silent. (If she tells you to shut up, you're simply doing it wrong. So go get some lessons!)

For most women, silent sex is *boring*. **Images bring guys off, talk brings women off.** That's just the way it is.

It's very hard for a woman's brain to let her relax into her sexual body feelings and trust that being 'off guard' as a BELOVED will be OK. That's why so many women sometimes start thinking about the laundry or tomorrow's meeting and all kinds of other stuff while you're trying your best to bring her off. Women can't help it. It's the way Nature made their brains.

So, the LOVER has to relax her and then gently **grab her erotic attention** and *concentrate* it firmly and exclusively on her *here-and-now sexual pleasure.* And keep it there - for as long as you've both agreed the Love Practice sex session will last.

The way to do that is to **TALK TO HER.** If you don't know how already, get some expert to teach you and practice until you're ***real good*** at sexy talk. Gourmet LOVERS give good gourmet talk.

If you want to see an almost perfect example of a Master *professional* GOURMET LOVER relax and focus a woman on her own orgasmic pleasure – even under very tense and difficult circumstances – watch the Palm Beach Trick section of the movie *American Gigolo* with Richard Gere on video or DVD.

I could write a very long and erudite academic book doing a microscopic analysis of Gere's Erotic Mastering technique as demonstrated in these few minutes on celluloid. Or teach an intensive **year-long course**.

There are only two of his verbal interventions which I, as an Expert Love Coach, could help him to improve - for even more intense orgasmically ecstatic results. If you decide to study this champion model example of erotic mastery, try to figure out which these may be? (The clues are everywhere.)

The most important thing to remember therefore about differences in erotic gender hardwiring is that **women need to hear words** from their LOVERS.

They need to be **RELAXED** by their **LOVERS**. With touch. With the right erotic attitude. And with *words*. For most women having sex without commentary is as dull as it is for most men watching sport on TV without commentary.

Your mastery of erotic commentary will help your BELOVED concentrate on her body's orgasm sensations in riding the waves of erotic pleasure. (A deep slow voice, of course, is the sexiest.)

What does a LOVER say to a BELOVED? **Don't** tell her that she's beautiful – all women are trained to think they're ugly. Just like most men worry about their penises' performance and/or size.

If you tell her she's beautiful you set off some kind of inner argument in your BELOVED's head. You don't want to do that. You want her relaxed and focused exclusively on what you are erotically *doing* to her. Paying attention to your voice, your body and your erotic potency.

Guys usually worry that their cocks are too small and girls usually worry that their bodies are too big. That's all the result of a wicked con. *We've simply been trained to think that way in order to prevent us having as much orgasmic sexual body happiness as we want whenever we want.*

As I've explained, any man with a penis longer than 2-and-a-half inches is OK – especially if he knows what he's doing. *With his hands.*

And for **whatever** female body shape, there is some other body (or bodies) in the world just *craving* it sexually – *exactly as it is.* Human desire comes in even more varieties than the incredibly rich wonderful varieties of the erotic world of animals and insects. (For this purpose I also love the book by Katherine Gates on '*Deviant Desires - Incredibly Strange Sex*').

500lb women, women with amputations, women who have unusually formed genitals - you name it. Somebody out there wants YOU. Just as you are. I think I have seen contact advertisements for *just about **every possible thing** women may have been told (by other people) is 'wrong' with them.

I don't want to dignify the ridiculous and ubiquitous bum-size question with much of a response. Suffice it to say that all the best *sensationally sensual* BLACK BELT EROTIC MASTERS I have ever met or read about, want a **woman's buttocks on a woman**. Large, shapely, fleshy, rounded, soft. Dress designers, on the other hand, are not exactly well-known for preferring women as *their* BELOVEDS.......

You can off-load a piece from www.physis.co.uk which I wrote for Cosmopolitan on *Learning to Love Your Body* if you're a woman to help yourself. (They didn't publish it.) If you're a man, give it to a woman you love. (Somebody else advised me to take out the bit about the butt plug. You can ask me by e-mail if you really want to know.....)

There's **nothing** terribly wrong with our bodies as long as we can orgasm. If we can't orgasm, now *that's* terrible. Fortunately we all can because it's a NATURAL REFLEX. As long as we get the anatomy and the technique right.

So, tell her she's beautiful *for you.* Tell her how her bottom **turns *you* on.** Tell her *you* like the shape of her breasts. Tell her how wonderful it feels *to you* to be stroking her skin. Etc. etc. etc. Do not be afraid of repeating yourself. ***Give her an ATTENTION BATH.***

But be honest. Focus on the truth about *your erotic arousal* in looking at her, smelling her, touching her. She must be turning you on, otherwise you wouldn't be doing this would you?

Tell her how you absolutely **adore** seeing your BELOVED lose her customary self-control into the orgasmic sexual pleasure you are MAKING her feel. (I ***know*** that's true because thousands of honest men have told me this in confidence.)

It's absolute *erotic magic* when a man, seeing, hearing and feeling a woman nearing her climax instructs her masterfully: **"Come for me now!"** It's gets even better when he says: *"And again!" Harder! Louder! And come for me again!"*

How to *make* her come? Here's how: You start by sitting very comfortably and relaxed with your back against some pillows. It's quite good to try this out first by sitting on a couch with her seated between your legs. Logistically this makes the best engineering sense anyway.

You must make sure her bottom with all its erogenous zones is tight up against your cock so that *you can feel with your own body* almost exactly what she is experiencing – and the rest…

Most women just love the feeling of being comfortably enclosed and held in this way against their man's chest. She's offering herself to her LOVER in her most total sexual vulnerability. It's sexy and erotic and safe and relaxing. All at the same time. For a woman to be able to **lean into her LOVER's body** like this.

It's also comfortable and not tiring for the LOVER in this position on a couch. (Bed sex can get *so* boring). The LOVER is then usually able to put his (or her) hands easily round The BELOVED's waist and stimulate her whole clitoris for *a long time.* Whatever time period you both agreed for the Love Practice Sex Session. Or until she **begs** you to stop.

The LOVER places his wrist securely and firmly on the top part of the BELOVED woman's clitoris where it is just under her skin around her pubic bone. The LOVER then spreads his fingers confidently apart, two on each side, with a gap in the middle where the vagina is located.

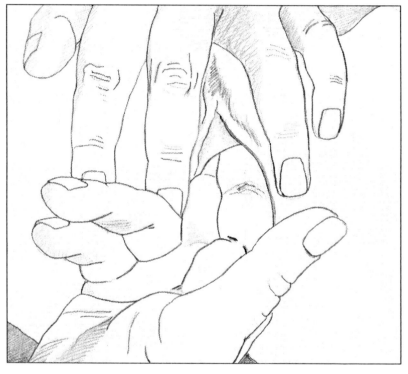

The Clarkson BLISS Position

©PHYSIS 2002

This is so that the BELOVED can feel him press on the '*crura*' – the wings of the clitoris which run just under the skin around and on the **outside** of her vagina on either side spreading into her thighs. It is perfectly possible to **feel** the shape and erect texture of the clitoris some 3mm just below the skin - once you know the anatomical shape of it.

The LOVER then places his other hand to rest on top of the anchor which he has made with the heel of his hand (near the top of the clitoris and over her pubic bone.)

This should leave two fingers of the LOVER's top hand comfortably free to go into her vagina, touching the tiny clit-end with your palm indirectly and hooking your two fingers round, like a beckoning sign, onto the clitoral promontory, otherwise known as the G-spot *inside* the vagina. Unlike the illustration, your two hands are resting on top of each other.

> If you have *any doubt whatsoever* about your hygiene or the smoothness of your skin, wear a sensitive surgical rubber glove on the hand you use to put inside her vagina to stimulate her clitoris from there.

You'll be pulling your BELOVED'S body very lovingly close to your own body in this way. She'll be *trusting* you to allow her to be *this* vulnerable to your sexual touch.

She'll be able to feel your heartbeat and your breathing through her back. You'll be able to feel *her* heartbeat and her breathing through your chest, arms, hands, thighs - *and your penis.* I promise.

Your bodies will be just about **blending together** like in those physics illustrations I showed in chapter 1. *Perfect for attunement at all levels.* Your mouth can be ready to kiss her shoulders and neck.

Most women ADORE this anyway. Some experts think that's because the nerve endings of the clitoris extend through the nipples to the neck. And I am personally sure they don't suddenly stop there either!

Frequently interspersed, of course, by your sexy talk breathed into her *left* ear. And *vice versa* if she's left handed. That's to do with stimulating her right brain hemisphere's activity which Nature designed to focus on shapes, rhythms, physical sensations and other kinds of sensual creative non-linear sexy erotic stuff.

The best **body movement** is to gently rock your pelvis (and your LOVE MUSCLES) backwards and forwards in a very SLOW rhythm. With her sitting between your legs she will have to follow your body's lead – as in dancing.

This pelvic rocking movement for both of you (a) builds the erotic 'charge' in each of your bodies' sexual orgasmic centres, (b) comforts, reassures and relaxes your 'inner animals', and (c) attunes to Nature's eternal pattern for ecstasy of steadily and completely breathing-in and breathing-out. **Nice and slow.** Completely in and completely out. No strain. Natural. Bodies LIKE doing this.

If your BELOVED is unused to you or someone else erotically *loving* this G spot of her clitoris inside with the pads of about two fingers in a circular motion rhythmically and steadily, she may at first feel like she's going to pee. This is a very good sign. She has reached her first ecstatic orgasmic *threshold*.

Reassure your BELOVED that she can tolerate this uncomfortable moment which is so intensely exciting *for you*. Tell her it's OK if she did pee. (You've put a towel underneath.) Continue the loving stroking like you would stroke a little kitten - and very very soon she will start orgasming with her whole body.

The movement of **any body** in full orgasmic ecstatic orgasm is like the undulating coils of a snake. It's much harder for the body to make this natural movement if there is something (or somebody) heavy on top of you. It's obviously better for the BELOVED to have room to move their body in Nature's natural orgasmic rhythm.

Keep rocking your pelvises slowly backwards and forwards like in a profoundly sexual natural dance. Your slow complete breathing-in and completely breathing-out will *naturally* synchronise. Be on standby for spontaneous massive extended or multiple orgasms. Just keep going – but avoid at all costs touching the by-now oversensitive little clit-end directly. Indirect stimulation round it is better.

If your BELOVED starts rubbing her clitoris against your hand herself, that's the best. Just let her. Your BELOVED's body knows exactly how she would like to take her pleasure from you. (Whatever her 'mind' says.) Don't get in her body's way by pushing, poking or prodding at her clitoris – inside or out.

Hold your hands still, firm against her and steady – but in **constant contact**. Tell her how much this is turning you on – seeing her *'go for'* her own pleasure using your hands. Let her take responsibility for her orgasm. Egg her on in any way you know how.

Your BELOVED **needs** to know *from you* that she is erotically exciting and pleasing you by doing this. Most women are trained to want to please men. Paradoxically, most women also believe that most men are very selfish lovers – the old 'men are only out for their own satisfaction' routine.

I *know* that this is NOT TRUE. Too many men have told **me** in personal and professional situations that their greatest sexual joy comes from making their woman come. I believe them. I have also experienced the **manly truth** of this in my own body, mind and soul many times. But most women haven't. This is *your chance* to convince her. Take it!

Do **not** be surprised if she ejaculates a little – or an enormous amount of - clitoris cream. It is *not* urine. It's just the same stuff as a man ejaculates, made by similar glands in our bodies, just without the sperm. (I love the word the Victorian pornographers used for it – 'spending'.)

This makes perfect anatomical sense if we remember that the clitoris and the penis are basically the *same sex organ.* Therefore they would, of course, work in a similar way!

Try it... If this CLARKSON BLISS POSITION doesn't work the first time, improve your stroking technique – or the music - or the erotic atmosphere – or your concentration. Get some coaching. Then, practice, practice, practice.

Of course, just like with a trainee aeroplane pilot, it's best to practice until you're perfect on a **simulator** like Jenteal *before* you try it on a *real* woman for the best chance of first time and regular success.

Many lovers have been ***utterly amazed*** at what ecstatic perfection this erotic technique can achieve. The LOVER feels like **THE GREATEST LOVER IN THE WHOLE WORLD.** The BELOVED goes into Orgasm Heaven.

And the BELOVED can come and come and come for hours! Just remember to rest every 50 minutes or so for a little while. Drink water, fruit juice, smoke. Whatever. Don't touch each other in the break time. And then slowly and deliberately start again. It simply works better that way.

SEX IS GOOD FOR PEOPLE. BETTER SEX IS BETTER.

QUALITY SEX MAKES FOR QUALITY LIFE.

When your agreed time for the Love Practice Sex Session is up, (or when she's tired from coming so much) ***don't*** suddenly stop. Gradually fade out the music your hands are making on her *whole* clitoris. Take your hands away very gently and slowly.

Continue to hold your BELOVED against you. Tell her what a fantastic experience that was for you. (I know it will be.) Congratulate her on her erotic talent for ecstatic surrender. Then you can be silent until she falls asleep or wants to do something else. Offer her some water, or a piece of fruit.

When she falls asleep, having drained out the last sensational drops of her orgasmic pleasure, cover her up with something warm and comfortable. Make sure your BELOVED is neither too warm nor too hot.

Stroke her hair and face. Stay physically close until she loses consciousness in a blissful sleep. If she hasn't done so already. Very strong intense massive orgasms can make women faint clean away from ecstasy. (Even the Victorians knew that!)

Don't worry about this *unless* she stops breathing. In which case do mouth-to-mouth resuscitation or call an ambulance immediately. Of course, not all women will faint. (I just said that to get your attention again.)

As female BELOVEDS build up more and more tolerance for ecstasy from experiencing it in massive and reliable doses, they will get used to the **intensity** of their erotic experience and will *want* to learn how to handle it even better.

Good LOVERS can learn to ride the ecstatic peaks and troughs with them and can have surprisingly unexpected orgasms too – without themselves even being touched. Male multiples are not unknown in this erotic trance state.

Such are the miracles of modern science.

! Don't ever let a doctor or a therapist of any description touch you *sexually*. Whatever Colombo, Freud, Jung, Perls, Berne, Kahn, Laing, and other doctors have done in the past, this kind of behaviour is always UNETHICAL and invariably BAD for the patient in the long run.

* There are just about a million variations on the CLARKSON BLISS POSITION which you can *creatively compose* for yourselves now that you know the basics. You can, for example, also try a pinky around or even inside her nerve rich anus. DO NOT **ever** force this on her if she really doesn't want to experiment with it.

? Hippocrates, Galen, Rufus of Ephesus, Julius Polux, the Arab anatomists Abulcassis and Avicenna, Hippocrates and Gabrielle Fallopio all already described the female clitoris hundreds of years ago. Why do you think this information has been hidden?

Chapter 8

Ecstasy – or getting high...

*"There is a way of breathing
that's a shame and a suffocation
And there's another way of expiring,
A Love Breath
That lets us open infinitely."* [13]

There are two major approaches to **ecstatic spiritual orgasmic sexual ecstasy.** Hindu Tantra (including the Kama Sutra), Chinese Sexual Kung Fu and the Christian Karezza are the major forms of approaches which teach learning advanced breathing techniques, meditation and control of male (and/or female) ejaculation for spiritual purposes.

I have studied and practised all of these for many years and they have great advantages for some people sometimes. As far as I am concerned, there are only two major drawbacks to them: (a) Their sexual anatomy is scientifically wrong and (b) they assume that ecstatic sex is not natural and innately spiritual anyway. I *know* that it is.

A female dolphin who orgasms (demonstrates all the outward signs of ecstatic sexual pleasure) by rubbing her belly flesh against another female dolphin does it simply because *it's natural and it feels good* for both of them. **Without such pleasures, who could bear the inevitable fears and pains of being a creature on this planet?**

The Clarkson Institute approach is NATURAL, RELATIONSHIP BASED and WHOLISTIC. It *integrates* the physical, emotional, communicative, ethical, cognitive, imaginative and spiritual levels of the BELOVED **and** the LOVER.

---

[13] Rumi

My approach to orgasmic ecstasy is a development well **beyond Tantra** or Taoist type sex which both (a) depend on male ejaculatory control, (b) takes years to master (c) wrongly teaches that the clitoris is a 'tiny bump' and (d) has little to offer the woman or the man in terms of NATURAL multiple physically based ecstatic orgasms *at all levels* simultaneously.

For only one other example: A well-known Taoist approach to orgasmic ecstasy teaches that a woman's sexual energy resides in her menstrual blood. I think somebody should tell this man that many women, even after hysterectomies and the menopause, often have **much more orgasmic sexual energy** than they had ever experienced in their lives before. Why, the forties and fifties are the period of life when many women only *begin* to hit their sexual stride. Just ask any of the thousands of younger men who benefit from this!

Anyway, the Clarkson Institute's approach honours the *animal* creature in each of us. (We share some 95% of our DNA with mice.) My approach is based simply on an accurate understanding of what NATURE has given us in our bodies **and** thinking this through logically to Orgasmic Sexual Love Practices which can work for anybody – whatever faith they believe in. Or not.

These two major kinds of approaches to ecstatic sexuality reflect two major approaches in counselling and psychotherapy. (a) *Change your thoughts* - and what you do and experience might change; and (b) *Change what you do* - and what you experience (and think) might change.

I think and feel these different approaches are both valid in certain circumstances depending on people's preferences. The case for the first approach has been much mystified and overstated. The rich, fast, varied and *easy* options in the second (and Nature's oldest) approach has, as far as I know, **never** been explained before.

Natural processes such as sexual ecstasy come from archaic regions of evolution in our DNA which encode the **wisdom of NATURE** accumulated over billions and billions of years.

ECSTATIC SEX IS OUR BIRTHRIGHT AS HUMAN ANIMALS.

Non-reproductive orgasming is our '*first* nature'. Just like male orgasm without ejaculation is first nature. For a man, learning how to orgasm with ejaculation is 'second nature' – something he got conditioned to later.

Just think about it. If Nature (or God or Evolution) meant sex to be only for reproduction of the species, there would be no other orgasmic sexual activity except that which is designed for making babies of one kind or another (penis in vagina sex).

*We now **know** for sure* that the natural world is saturated with examples of sexual activity by many species of all kinds which does **not** result in the making of babies. Read *Dr Tatiana's Sex Advice to All Creation* - just for starters - if you don't believe me.

If Nature meant orgasmic sex to be only for reproduction of the human species, human females would only come on heat (be available for sex) during the times they could conceive, wouldn't they?

This would mean that there would be only two or three days a month (from around 13 years of age) to the menopause (from around 45 years onwards) when women would be interested in sex.

That means only 96 days out of some 31,755 days *in a whole lifetime* for a woman – **if** she never fell pregnant. An Anglophone woman's average life expectancy is now estimated to be 87 years. I think 96 orgasms in a whole lifetime is a miserly starvation ration.

OBVIOUSLY, *from an evolutionary point of view, reproduction of the species is a very, very **minor** purpose of orgasmic sex.* The major purpose of sex is play: pleasure, comfort, intimacy, bonding, excitement, stimulation, stress relief, fun, enhancing the immune system, keeping physically, emotionally and spiritually fit and experiencing large chemical doses of NATURAL ORGASMIC ECSTASY.

"He [Ulrich Gerhardt] did important work on the genitorenal physiology of mammals, always trying to unite structure and function. In studying the evolutionary origins of vertebrate genitourinary function, he investigated the reproductive biology of spiders and slugs. During most of his life he sought evidence for his belief in orthogenesis (the doctrine that evolution proceeds in a purposeful, productive sequence of improvements) but finally (and, I believe, reluctantly) he concluded that within the endless variety of life and sexual structures there are many features which offer no clear advantage but are sportive, random, and merely decorative. Nature is not only red in tooth and claw but also giggles, plays, and acts silly." (p. 63 in Lowry) Or, as Heraclitus said: **Physis [Nature] is a child at play**.

In a nutshell: *The major purpose of sex* is to give us the **ecstatic drug trips** created by the pain-killing and feelgood natural hormones which our bodies release in extended pleasure (endorphins, amongst others).

I think and feel it's the very least Nature could do for us - given everything else we have to cope with. In the words of a poet, we humans are *"the most wretched creatures who ever crawled upon the earth"*.

Don't **you** think and feel we deserve all the ecstasy we can get? And, *obviously*, if we don't get it naturally, we'll take it any damn way we can get it. Even in a pill called Ecstasy. Needing ECSTASY is just *Human Nature*.

So, here's one **recipe for ecstatic orgasmic sex** based on the best current scientific information:

Plan it. Arrange the love practice sex session at least a week in advance. **If** you don't plan it as meticulously and painstakingly as you planned and prepared for *your first date* with someone you really fancied, **rehearse** various scenario's of what you will do when the opportunity presents itself, so that you are fit and ready to make the most of it 'spontaneously'. (Ha!)

Planning includes selecting the place, the costumes, the desired equipment, the hygiene and safety precautions, the starting and finishing times, minimising or controlling possible interruptions, creating 'the kind of mood' you want, as well as being 'fit for it' by warming up physically, emotionally, mentally, spiritually, intellectually and in fantasy. Just a similar process you go through before you engage in any serious sport. You don't just run onto the pitch 'spontaneously' and start scoring goals! It is **planned.**

A professional Gigolo once told me that the major ingredient in sexually arousing a woman is building her *erotic anticipation*. I can personally vouch for that! Planning, preparing and getting ready for a party - or a football game - is usually the best guarantee of pleasurable success. The best sex at night starts at breakfast – or a week before.

Of course there's no law against quickies! But don't confuse them with your seriously important LOVE PRACTICE sex sessions. That's what sorts the 'wham-bam bonkers' from the Gourmet LOVERS.

Timing. Men's sexual hormones peak around 7 in the morning and women's sexual hormones peak around 9 in the morning. This is the scientific information. Figure out for yourself *what time of the day* **you are most likely to have NATURALLY ecstatic orgasmic sex.**

We don't yet know exactly how long it takes of sensual sexual activity before your whole body begins to fully **experience** the release of the our natural ecstatic chemicals, but we know that the beneficial effects can last for days.

It seems that many people can feel 'the full-on hit', on average after 20 minutes of coming. Then it's up to you how long you want to continue experiencing THE ECSTATIC FLOW. Stop if you've had enough, but 50 minutes is the recommended time – just like in football matches. Then both of you need to take a 10 or 15 minute break if you want more. That gives the brain time to process and integrate the experience before you start again. Unlike going to the gym, *you **cannot overdose** on natural orgasmic sexual ecstasy.*

Most of us remember those **intense** periods of *ecstatic erotic FEASTS* when we were first freely sexually active with a new lover we had really lusted after. *"It went on for days and nights... we were utterly absorbed in each other... we never stopped touching...we forgot to eat... we hardly ever slept... yet we were amazingly energetic and creative..."*

That's just Nature's way of showing us what's **possible.** So that we will remember. And do it again and again and again. With different people or with the same partner for as long as we want to. For as long as we live.

Don't worry about controlling your breathing – or your ejaculations. Hard-ons and ejaculations are irrelevant for ecstatic sexual orgasms. Erections may come and go. Orgasms just come and come and come.

Our bodies have millions of years of training of exactly how to breathe in sexually ecstatic states in our DNA. As soon as you begin to feel the natural feel-good chemicals 'hit', your breathing will **absolutely naturally** start doing exactly the right thing.

Listen for the noises to start from deep within the centre of your being. Continue to let the universal sounds and movements of orgasm to emerge *out of* your belly. ALLOW THIS NATURAL FLOW. *Surrender* to the rhythm of the Universe. And the sound of it too. If you're with a safe and trustworthy LOVER, the very worst that can happen is an extended experience of being in ecstatic orgasmic *HEAVEN.*

Sexual fitness: In both women and men the most important muscles for sexual fitness are the Pelvic Floor muscles. The stronger and fitter these LOVE MUSCLES are, the better, longer and more intense and the more multiple and/or extended orgasms you will experience.

Keeping these pelvic floor muscles fit also have the *additional advantages* of (a) definitely reducing women's urine stress incontinence now and later; (b) certainly tightening the pussy thereby intensifying your man's pleasure; (c) exercising and toning the whole clitoris for multiple orgasms and (d) *perhaps* even reducing the incidence of prostrate cancer in men.

Research funding is needed for *proving* the latter hypothesis, but it seems to make anatomical sense to me. Not to mention that real fit LOVE MUSCLES are also (a) good for your posture, (b) cures many kinds of backache, (c) is wonderful for self-confidence as well as (d) inducing a daily moment-by-moment experience of **natural well-being.**

You can practice the famous Kegel exercises pulling your genital sphincters really really tight a hundred times at least three times a day. There are basically three *movements*: (a) gently pulsing; (b) hard pulsing; (c) clenching. (It's a great thing to do while commuting or in boring meetings. No one else ever has to know!)

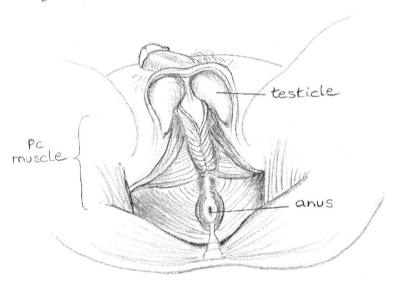

Love Muscles

And two *directions*: (a) upwards into the pelvis as high as you can go without moving your stomach muscles; and (b) downwards as if you're expelling an egg or giving birth. Combine these for best results in whatever patterns take your fancy.

You could even start experimenting with cyclic patterns. I personally just LOVE clenching my anal, vaginal, urethral and clitoral sphincters first separately and then all four together in a kind of progressive circular motion backwards and forwards - just following the contours of the **pelvic floor hammock of muscles** down below.

And/or you can invest in a female Pelvic Floor Exerciser available from any chemist. It should ALWAYS be recommended by medical staff in cases of urinary incontinence, after giving birth and hysterectomies AND in all cases where women are 'anorgasmic' or 'lack sexual desire'.

It's a discreet tampon shaped device with little weights inside who'll do the exercises *for you*. You won't even feel it inside the vagina. It just gently reminds those muscles of their function and exercises them for you - while you get on with your other business.

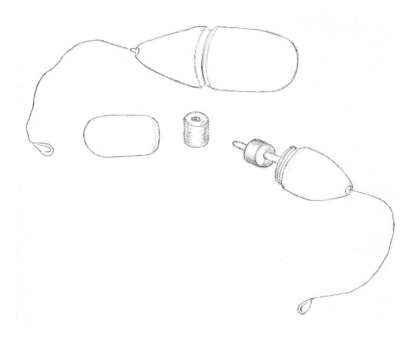

Female Love Muscle Exerciser

All a woman has to do is put it inside her vagina just like a tampon. For as long as she wants to. Every day for at least three weeks. (I wear mine comfortably for days on end.) The woman can measure her own increasing SEX MUSCLE FITNESS levels by graduating progressively from the larger one with lighter weights to the thinner one with the heavier weights. And then she'll begin feel the undeniable difference in the intensity of her orgasms....... And want more.

All a man has to do for similar ecstatic orgasmic effects is strap a similar pelvic floor exercising device around his penis and balls on the outside. The equivalent for men, available from any good sex shop, looks something like this:

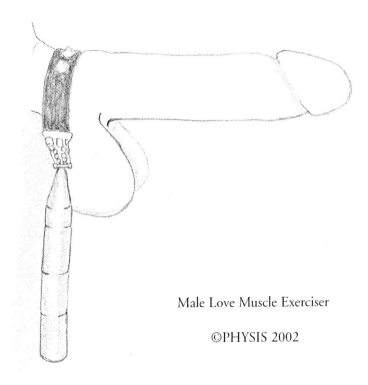

Male Love Muscle Exerciser

©PHYSIS 2002

Just like in any other kind of physical weight training, you start with the lightest weight which comfortably exercises the relevant muscle group. Then you add the next weight. Then you build up to whatever level of sexual muscle fitness you choose – flabby couch potato genitals, club league packet or world class championship standard LOVE MUSCLES.

It's your choice. What grade and purity of Sexual Ecstasy you want in your life. And for how long you want to take it. This pleasure is FREE. To anyone. No matter what they look like and no matter how young or how old they are. Ecstatic orgasm is *the* **gateway drug** to heavenly bliss on earth and lifelong experiences of unexpected spiritual fulfilment.

Positions: Here there's only one rule for a BELOVED: Whatever ecstatic body position turns you on in which you can stay – without cramping or danger - for at least 90 minutes.

The only rule for a LOVER: never be outside of lunging distance, i.e. the distance it would take to act swiftly on the BELOVED's body in case of an emergency.

Ethics: There are three essential rules: SAFETY, SANITY and CONSENT.

If you don't know what SAFETY means in a sexual context, you had better find out pronto. Or contact the British Medical Association for detailed instructions.

SANITY means nobody is involved who is drunk, stoned or otherwise likely to be *under the influence* of extreme emotions such as rage or panic or grief or revenge. ***This is a sexual ecstasy only zone.***

This is another reason why mornings are often the best – chances are you're not drinking by then. By the way, even *driving a car* under the influence of extreme emotions could expose the driver to a charge of culpable homicide in the event of an accident. Don't do it!

CONSENT means *nobody* is involved - in any way - who is not legally, mentally or emotionally competent to give consent **and** who has not *explicitly* given their verbal consent. Getting and giving consent can be done beautifully and erotically in thousands of exciting ways.

For example, one man I know always asks his BELOVED to put his penis inside her vagina **with her own hands** if she wants him inside her. Another man almost always asks when he moves onto a new activity:

"Do you want me to stop doing what I'm doing? Yes or No?"

He insists on a shake or a nod from his BELOVED as evidence of her consent for each new sexual activity he explores with her. Psychologically this makes her erotically complicit and responsible **with him** making her TAKE her pleasure. All I know is that it is *damn sexy* the way he does it to me.

Ecstatic Sex is **impossible** without proper genuine consent. This may require explicitly agreeing with each other beforehand that *"No! Please don't!"* means *"Yes, please continue"* but that the word: *RED!* means *"Stop what you're doing to me immediately now"*.

An *integrative* approach to NATURAL ecstatic spiritual sexuality therefore includes simultaneously (a) our animal physiology; (b) our emotional states; (c) our words and images;(d) our ethics and values; (f) our rational or scientific information; (g) our particular human need for *making meaning* (imagining) as well as (h) a transcendent spiritual dimension.

In ecstatic orgasmic sexual states, all of these co-exist as a brief moment of eternity and we experience the greatest heaven which is possible for human being on earth. No one level is better or 'higher' than any other. *Each level has its own beauty.* Indeed for wholistic sex, they are all played together in infinite exquisiteness as the seven colours of the rainbow or the notes of the octave.

Of course, there can be no words to adequately describe the experience. That's why I call it 'trans-personal'. People can understand transpersonal any way they want to. (a) Spiritually (b) artistically or (c) through the natural sciences such as quantum physics and complexity science.

> **! CAUTION:** Lovers should *never* rely on the BELOVED being able to consciously remember a 'safe word' in extended orgasmic ecstatic states. These are all about getting *out* of ordinary consciousness. Use your own common sense, your physiological information and your constant

intentional empathic awareness of your BELOVED's body.

* Most of Sexual Gourmet or Sexual Ecstasy Education is about **un-learning** old prejudices, body armouring, defensiveness, lies we've been told and have believed. *The sun does not revolve around the earth, the earth revolves around the sun.* We are looking at a similar revolution in our understanding of sexuality on earth. Standby for lift-off!

? If you have found other recipes for *reliably* getting your sex orgasmic ecstasy high, please e-mail me about them so that I can keep the world informed of all our possible options for earthly bliss.

Chapter 9

If you want to make babies...

The kiss.

There is strange, and not yet strange, is the kiss. It is strange because it mixes silliness with tragedy, and yet not strange because there is good reason for it. There is shaking by the hand. That should be enough. Yet a shaking of hands is not enough to give a vent to all kinds of feeling. The hand is too hard and too used to doing all things, with too little feeling and too far from the organs of taste and smell, and far from the brain, and the length of an arm from the heart. To rub a rose like some people do is better, but there is nothing good to the taste about the nose, only a piece of old bone pushing out of the face, and a nuisance in winter, but a friend before meals and in a garden, indeed. With the eyes we can do nothing, for if we come too near, they go crossed and everything comes twice to the sight without good from one or other.

There is nothing to be done with the ear, so back we come to the mouth, and we kiss with the mouth because it is a part of the head and of the organs of taste and smell. It is the temple of the voice, keeper of breath and its giving out, treasurer of tastes and succulences, and a home of the noble tongue. And its portals are firm, yet soft, with a warmth, of a ripeness, unlike the rest of the face, rosy, and in women with a crinkling red tenderness, to the taste not in compare with the wild strawberry, yet if the taste of kisses went, and strawberries came the year round, half of joy would be gone from the world. There is no wonder to me that we kiss, for when mouth comes to mouth, in all its silliness, breath joins breath, and taste joins taste, warmth is enwarmed, and tongues commune in a soundless language, and those things are said that cannot find a shape, have a name, or know a life in the pitiful faults of speech. [14]

---

[14] Llewellyn, R., 1939, How green was my valley. London: New English Library

Kissing is **so** wonderful for humans that it has been known to lead to babies. Nobody must *ever* make unwanted babies. Babies must be made only if they are wanted. Carefully. Honestly. Responsibly. By at least two or more people who want to take proper care of them all the time until they are grown-up. The more people the better.

Even if there is a divorce. Whether two grown-ups want to make have sex with each other for all that time or not. The babies must be looked after by two or more people properly and lovingly until they are at least sixteen.

Maybe longer. By people who love Life. And who love orgasmic sex heaven in their bodies and minds and souls. Perhaps **baby-caring contracts between** the two or more people who make the baby are more important than a marriage ceremony? If almost half of marriages in the UK end in divorce perhaps it means that something is wrong with our *ideas of marriage.*

Perhaps it means that men and women still expect things from each other that are not possible anymore. Or never have been possible? Like life-long sexually intense faithfulness to one other person for everybody in the whole world. Our idealised romantic expectations of each other are so unrealistically high, they're almost bound to end in bitterness and disappointment.

Perhaps that's why so many men are frightened of women. Or why so many women are angry with men. And also perhaps why there is so much depression, '*extreme sadness*', horrible divorces and confused children and suicidal teenagers.

Of course there are exceptions to any rule. If you're one of those lucky exceptions in a life-long monogamous erotically orgasmic marriage, don't worry. *Expecting* one other person to fulfil all your emotional, financial, spiritual, sexual, fantastical, ethical needs for all of your life – and you theirs – is not unusual. Being humanly capable of both people *delivering* it is exceptionally rare.

All babies deserve that they are not born into unrealistic psychological marriage contracts built on fairy tale romances, **Bride Today** and **Hello Magazine** pictures of celebrities. (And we all know about that curse!) But that **doesn't** mean we can't have orgasmic sexual heaven as much or as often as anybody likes. Sanely, safely and consensually.

Orgasmic sexual heaven for **every body** means not making unwanted babies through misunderstandings and believing lies about baby-making sex being the best for most people. It isn't.

However, once two adults have decided to make a baby together and can realistically undertake the very big commitment of taking care of their child for the next 18 years at least, they should have some fun making the baby too. I think that's only fair, don't you?

When a **woman is on top of the man** she can come by rubbing herself on his pelvic bone better than from almost any other position with his penis inside her vagina to catch the baby-making sperm. With some object like a pillow between their legs, this position is also one which the many women first use to masturbate. (Note that pillows are not particularly known for being 'hard'.) Many men also like the woman-on-top position for genital intercourse because it's less work for them and they can then concentrate on their own erotic feelings.

This is what Lillith, Adam's first wife did. They did sex intercourse with Lillith on top. One of the Gods who didn't like sex, called Jehovah, sent Lillith away from paradise for coming to orgasm like this. At least that's one story.

Another good way for a woman to come to orgasm heaven while wanting to make babies is if a man does sex intercourse with a woman in '**doggie-style**'. This is where the woman makes herself bend down on her hands and knees like our monkey ancestors did. She comes better from this baby-making work of love because the man can then use his penis better to stimulate the whole clitoris inside her directly *through the walls of her vagina*.

This angle means that he is probably bumping his penis on the peak of the inside clitoris mountain which some people call the G-point. (It's better if he also goes circular or from side to side if he can. If his LOVE MUSCLES are fit enough!) If the man puts his flat hand on her clit-end at the same time their *coming* can simply be off-scale. But often that's not even necessary for heavenly coming - as you will find out.

Another position which some people like is called *the missionary position.* The only problem with this is that's it real hard for most normal women to get their orgasms from this position. That only makes sense. It's nice enough for the guy, but doesn't do much for the lady.

So as I've explained in Chapter 8, this is why the missionary position is NOT so good for a woman's orgasms in baby-making sex. You see the sticky-out part of the clitoris (which is like Nature's road sign to point in the *right* **direction**) lifts up and away when it gets sexually excited. (Furthermore the vaginal walls 'tent' away – balloon outwards.)

So during baby-making sex in the missionary position the woman's clitend lifts up and away from where the penis goes into the vagina. Furthermore a man's penis going in and out of a vagina (because that's the movement most men like best) simply just misses the stimulation of the clitoris - which is physically located in the woman's body *above* (where he's usually pushing) and going down into her thighs.

I can't tell you how many men have sat in my consulting room puzzled by sexperts' instructions to watch their women masturbate - in order to learn how to make their come. When I ask them specifics, they demonstrate their women's masturbation techniques to me with the rubber dolls or Jenteal.

How long does it take her to come to orgasm when she masturbates? 30 seconds to five minutes. Does she use a penis-sized object for penetrating her vagina? No. Does she use her hand? If yes, we've hit paydirt. Put *your hand* on top of hers and imitate her movements and rhythm until you're as good or better than she.

He says: No hands, I ask, what does she *actually* do? He most often then says she lies on her side, puts a pillow tightly between her thighs and rocks her pelvis gently backwards and forwards on it until she orgasms.

Now, they ask me where does my penis even begin to figure in that? Well, it doesn't.

Female masturbation

This is actually quite a common and effective way for many women to masturbate to orgasm. And if you get a woman really hot, she'll do it on your hand, forearm or your thigh too! (No need for a hard-on anywhere else!) She's obviously stimulating her whole clitoris herself *from the outside*.

The only way a LOVER can technically improve on the remarkable efficiency of this anatomically accurate female masturbation technique is to use fingers to stimulate her whole clitoris from the inside *as well*. **The best loving always involves another person.** I think that was Nature's idea. But not always in the way a man thinks it *should* be.......

So, unless a man has got a very *big* body and/or she keeps her thighs really TIGHT together during missionary position intercourse the woman's sexual organ won't get stimulated at all! And, as a North American love doctor put it: "**A penis banging up and down on a clitoris does nothing for a girl**".

(I'm not a love doctor. I'm a love coach.) In fact, a penis bobbing up and down on your clitoris is so *damn irritating* that two-thirds of Cosmopolitan-reading young women admit that they 'fake' orgasms. Well, so much for the success rate of that kind of magazine sex education!

Furthermore, remember that 80% of women don't enjoy orgasmic intercoursal sex with their partners anyway. You have enough information now to figure out for yourself the reason why.

There's one other solution for orgasmic baby-making sex with the man on top of the woman. It's called the CAT – or technically - the **Coital Alignment Technique**. It's quite difficult to explain without showing it on an actual man and woman's body or with inflatable models.

Anyway, I'll try. The man has to position his pelvis **above** the woman's pelvis so that his pelvic bone (which is covered with a handy cushion of fat) can rub on her whole clitoris (which is tucked around *her* pelvic bone) If he rocks gently backwards and forwards like this - not thrusting of course - she can sometimes come to massive orgasms like this.

Some men don't like this CAT baby-making sex position so much because their natural movement in intercourse is different, but it's great fun to experiment with it. Men usually like straight in and out movements and women usually like more circular round movements. You'll never know what *you* might like until you give it a try.

In conclusion, there's no denying that many people enjoy intercourse sex for many reasons - most of them psychological or social - it's simply just not the best and most reliable way of coming to ORGASM HEAVEN. Specially for most women on earth.

! **Do not ever** have baby-making sex *unless* you want to make babies - or a condom is worn. And make sure the condom is fresh and **new,** really **tough,** of the most expensive highest **quality** and that *no oil of any kind* gets anywhere near it.

* There are some statistically abnormal women (2 out of 10) who can easily have orgasms in other ways during conventional baby-making sex. The explanation for this appears to be that their clitoral anatomy and nerve-endings distribution are unusual.

? **Why** do you think they called it "the missionary position"?

Chapter 10

Where to go next and where to find out more...

'Then said Almitra, Speak to us of Love.
And he raised his head and looked upon the people,
And there fell a stillness upon them. And with a great voice he said:
When love beckons to you, follow him,
Though the sword hidden among his pinions may wound you.
And when he speaks to you believe in him,
Though his voice may shatter your dreams as the north wind lays
waste the garden.
For even as love crowns you so shall he crucify you. Even as he is for
your growth, so is he for your pruning.
Even as he ascends to your height and caresses your tenderest
branches that quiver in the sun.
So shall he descend to your roots and shake them in their clinging to
the earth.
Like sheaves of corn he gathers you unto himself.
He threshes you to make you naked.
He sifts you to free you from your husks.
He grinds you to whiteness.
He kneads you until you are pliant;
And then he assigns you to his sacred fire, that you may become
sacred bread for God's sacred feast.

All these things shall love do unto you that you may know the secrets
of your heart, and in that knowledge become a fragment of Life's
heart.' [15]

---

[15] Gibran, K. (1972) *The Prophet*, London: William Heinemann, pp. 7-8.

GO FIGURE SUMMARY:

- 80% of women do not orgasm from penis-in-vagina sexual intercourse alone
- Only 1.7% of women use anything for vaginal penetration to masturbate to orgasm
- A woman takes on average 30 seconds to 5 minutes to come to orgasm when she masturbates or is competently stimulated by a lover. Just the same as a man. (This is no surprise because the clitoris is the same organ as the penis.)
- 1 in 20 marriages are practically sexless after the first few years.
- 43% of adult British women have been found to suffer from 'lack of desire'.
- The most frequently asked question to Cosmopolitan in the USA is: *"How can I orgasm during intercourse?"*
- Two-thirds of Cosmopolitan readers in the UK have admitted that they 'fake' orgasms.
- Most multiply orgasmic lesbians rarely use vibrators or dildo's.
- The best-selling vibrators bought by women are the smallest ones.
- 1 in 3 British women report that they are too stressed or tired to have sex.
- 44% of British men report that they are too tired or stressed to have sex.
- Yet we KNOW that orgasm is the best natural stress reliever of all.

"What if all this 'dysfunction' is not so much a lack of interest in sex, but a lack of interest in the type of sex that society [and the Freudians] consider normal?" (Dr. Gloria Brame quoted in Lou Paget.)

All genuinely competent *and* confident golfers, managers, stockbrokers, chefs, or gardeners for that matter, are characterised by their desire to learn more and continually update and develop their performance.

Champions in any field become and remain champions *only for as long* as *they continue to practise and constantly improve under the supervision of the best coaches they can possibly afford.*

INFORMATION; COMMUNICATION; INITIATIVE: and IMAGINATION – these are the four key areas of development for anyone who wants to improve as a LOVER and/or as a BELOVED.

This book has focused mainly on INFORMATION and the distribution INITIATIVE. If you're a man, and if you want to learn in more detail from me about *'How to handle a woman'*, the book of this title is available from www.nospine.com. (Publishers have told me that English speaking men won't buy it. But it is out in Spanish!!)

The **scientific sexual anatomy** on which my Natural Sexual Ecstasy approach is based on is the most accurate current scientific information that I have been able to research in the world. And it is also continually updated as new research discoveries are made, or previous errors come to light.

I think that Plato was wrong about the mind/body split. I think and feel that human existence is a complex intermeshing of *seven* different levels of experience which co-exist and resonate together between two or more people in sexuality – amongst other things. (This is also based on sound scientific research and you can also read more about it from sources listed on www.physis.co.uk)

If you want to learn more about COMMUNICATION: read *"Everything you ever wanted to know about communication and were afraid to ask..."* available from www.nospine.com. E-mail me if there's anything else you want me to cover in the next edition of that book or in another publication.

PLEASE also remember that all the scientific research shows that more than 87% of communication is **non-verbal.** That's also why just reading this book is only some 13% of what I can convey in a workshop or in individual love coaching.

On COUPLES relationships you can read *"Everything you ever wanted to know about being in a couple and were afraid to ask…"* Available from www.nospine.com. E-mail me if there's anything else you want to know – or to tell me.

Regarding IMAGINATION: I look forward to finishing a book on *The Ecstatic Erotic Imagination* in the near future. E-mail me what you would like me to put in it. In the meantime – Read any or all of **Nancy Friday**'s most excellent and informative books on the topic as orgasmic ecstasy fantasy fertilizer.

Britain's *FIRST SEX SCHOOL* and the first sex school of its kind in the world, - of which I am the founder - can also be contacted via www.physis.co.uk.

We offer **Confidential Individual Gourmet Love Coaching** to men and women and in-betweens; and **Sexual Fitness Workshops** *for Men and Women separately.* You can see some testimonials on my website.

Experience has shown that Sex Education is much for effective – and fun – when we work with men and women SEPARATELY. Men think and feel differently about sex than most women. They also *talk* differently about it. This is supported by scientific evidence about brain differences between most men and most women. (Amongst other things.) Furthermore many couples report that they have 'talked sex to death' in their marriages – and in the counselling which they have attended *together.*

That's why I generally advise couples who want to improve their sex life, to *completely* cease *TALKING* about sex with each other *until* they have learnt and practiced how to do it WELL individually first. And that's only *after* they've learned how to bring each other to orgasm heaven. It's practically impossible for a man and a woman to communicate well *over* all the misinformation, mutual misunderstandings, anxieties and resentment which typically accumulate over the years between the couple to cloud the issue in most long-term relationships.

That's another bunch of reasons why separate Love Coaching for sex is necessary to start with. Prevention is always better than cure. So, *if* you're interested in improving the quality of your own love life, my professional advice is to start taking action yourself - with or without your partner's knowledge - NOW. Same applies if you want to prepare yourself sexually for your next partner before you even meet him or her.......... As the saying goes: *"When preparation meets opportunity, you have success."*

After an initial consultation, we will make referrals if appropriate to competent professionals whom, in the past, we have found to be ethical, well-informed, sex-affirmative and committed to staying up-to-date with accurate scientific information in their fields. *We take no responsibility for what decisions you make if you see them or take their advice, should you choose to follow it.*

We also hold a Register of qualified, sex-affirmative Relationship Psychology Counsellors and Sexual Ecstasy Coaches to whom we may make referrals on the same conditions.

There are, as yet, very few of these. However, *we do run trainings to Certificate and Diploma levels as well as supervise Doctoral students for people who want to professionally and/or academically qualify in these fields.* Please enquire.

World-wide e-mail consultations are also available and a *video-conferencing facility* for providing globally available consultations are being installed as I write this.

For detailed peer-reviewed information about how counselling, psychotherapy and psychoanalysis in the last hundred years – and to date - has avoided or *actively hindered* the development of a sex-affirmative culture and heavenly orgasms in the bedroom and elsewhere, please consult my academic papers which are available on request. And watch out for news about the press date of my soon *forthcoming* academic sex book which can be pre-ordered for speeded-up delivery from my site.

As I was finishing this book a friend sent me the following joke:

A man walking along a California beach was deep in prayer. All of a sudden, he said out loud, *"Lord , please grant me one wish."*

Suddenly the sky clouded above his head and in a booming voice the Lord said, *'because you have TRIED to be faithful to me in all ways, I will grant you one wish.'*

The man said, *"Build a bridge to Hawaii, so I can drive over anytime I want to."*

The Lord said, *"Your request is very materialistic. Think of the logistics of that kind of undertaking. The supports required to reach the bottom of the Pacific! The concrete and steel it would take! I can do it, but it is hard for me to justify your desire for worldly things. Take a little more time and think of another wish, a wish you think would honour and glorify me."*

The man thought about it for a long time. Finally he said, *"Lord, I wish that I could understand women. I want to know how they feel inside, what they are thinking when they give me the silent treatment, why they cry, what they mean when they say 'nothing', and how I can make a woman truly happy"*

After a few minutes God said, *"You want two lanes or four on that bridge?"*

But, when you're finished smiling in wry recognition, think about the fact that in this story, they're all **assuming** that God is a man.......

Finally, this is my wish for all humanity: That *we will MAKE LESS WAR AND MORE ORGASMIC ECSTASY !*

* There are probably hundreds of other *books* that will tell you how to improve your sex life in their different ways. However, if these manuals were working, how come 43% of adult British women are being diagnosed as suffering from FSD (Female sexual dysfunction)? Experiment until you find the way that works best for *you*.

? Why do you think so many people are very willing to invest in their sport or their businesses, but so reluctant to invest in their own and their partners' orgasmic sexual ecstasy and long term relational happiness?

CLARKSON COUPLES SEX WORKSHEET

Filled in fictional example

Each person to fill these in separately - and only then compare their lists. It's a great and comfortable way for finding out (a) what each other *will not do or have done to them*, (b) what each of you *would prefers to do or have done to them* and (c) what each of you would *like to try to do or try having done to them*. It also a good starting point for a fruitful relationship conversation or even attending a couples workshop or couples counselling if you want to.

A Issues which are non-negotiable = Grounds for leaving
(they are often surprisingly different for the two people in a couple)

HER	HER
1. Public humiliation – Their social circle finding out that he's been having sex with another woman	Infidelity – her having sex with any other man
2. Violence – any physical threat or attack	Verbally abusing him for being black, Jewish etc.
3. Wanting babies well before biological clock runs out	Not wanting children at all. Ever
4. No anal intercourse ever.	Not using a condom
5. Not telling her he has contracted a STD	Her publishing how lousy he is in bed

These are the **necessary** conditions for the *working alliance* between the two people to continue. They need to know what these issues are for themselves and inform their partners as early on in the relationship as possible. *Could you find subtle and comfortable ways of introducing these themes easily into your conversation on a first or second date?*

B Issues which are unchangeable = Aspects of SELF such as physiology (unchangeable by choice) or *sexual preferences*

HER	HER
1. Low sex drive	Needing to orgasm at least twice a week
2. Hating anilingus	Hating cunnilingus
3. Hating cunnilingus	Being officiously ordered around during sex
4. No intercourse during her period	Wearing women's panties to get aroused
5. Needing clitoral stimulation to orgasm	Looking at pornography

These are *unchangeable* aspects of self and sexuality. I consider it a violation of a person's basic human rights if anyone tries to change these. It's also a waste of time and energy. Anyway, one can try – but it won't work – not for long! You first fell in love with the person they are. Love *that* person.

C Issues which are negotiable = aspects of BEHAVIOUR

Behaviours which are up for give-and-take; turn-taking; compromise, erotic or sexual things which you would like to try or try having done to you etc. etc.

SHE WANTS AND HE WILL	HE WANTS AND SHE WILL
1. Give 'good talk' during sex	Dress up in erotic underwear for him
2. Give her an all-over body massage	A weekly blow-job

SHE WANTS AND HE WILL	HE WANTS AND SHE WILL
3. Him to remember anniversaries	Her to do watersports on him
4. Sex in public places	Video their sex for *private* consumption
5. Enact a stranger-fantasy in an hotel room	Enact his dominatrix fantasy (ropes & whips)

These are issues of sexual behaviour and conduct which you would like to experiment with. These issues alone are worth *both* of you investing feedback, emotional energy and intelligent problem-solving.

(This kind of information is best exchanged in the form of: When you *do*...........I *feel*; I would like you to change or improve what you DO in this way. In return I am willing to...........)

CLARKSON COUPLES SEX

Blank worksheet

Each person to fill these in separately - and only then compare their lists. It's a great and comfortable way for finding out (a) what each other *will not do or have done to them*, (b) what each of you *would prefers to do or have done to them* and (c) what each of you would *like to try to do or try having done to them*. It also a good starting point for a fruitful relationship conversation or even attending a couples workshop or couples counselling if you want to.

A Issues which are non-negotiable = Grounds for leaving
(they are often surprisingly different for the two people in a couple)

1.

2.

3.

4.

5.

These are the **necessary** conditions for the *working alliance* between the two people to continue. They need to know what these issues are for themselves and inform their partners as early on in the relationship as possible. *Could you find subtle and comfortable ways of introducing these themes easily into your conversation on a first or second date?*

B Issues which are unchangeable = Aspects of SELF such as physiology (unchangeable by choice) or ***sexual preferences***

1.

2.

3.

4.

5.

These are u*nchangeable* aspects of self and sexuality. I consider it a violation of a person's basic human rights if anyone tries to change these. It's also a waste of time and energy. Anyway, one can try – but it won't work – not for long! You first fell in love with the person they are. Love *that* person.

© & moral rights, P. Clarkson, PHYSIS, 2001.

C Issues which are negotiable = aspects of BEHAVIOUR

Behaviours which are up for give-and-take; turn-taking; compromise, erotic or sexual things which you would like to try or try having done to you etc. etc.

1.

2.

3.

4.

5.

These are issues of sexual behaviour and conduct which you would like to experiment with. These issues alone are worth *both* of you investing feedback, emotional energy and intelligent problem-solving.

(This kind of information is best exchanged in the form of: When you *do*...........I *feel*; I would like you to change or improve what you DO in this way. In return I am willing to...........)

© & moral rights, P. Clarkson, PHYSIS, 2001.

Services

*For confidential individual Love Coaching, or Sexual Gourmet classes, Sexual Fitness weekend workshops for men and for women, public talks, couples' consultation, relationship enrichment workshops, lectures, training and supervision, in person, by phone **or by e-mail***:

Professor Petruska Clarkson, Ph.D.,D. Litt. et Phil.
PHYSIS,
58 Harley Street,
London W1G 9QB

Fax: 020 7637 2760

Phone: 020 7436 6976

e-mail: petruska.c@dial.pipex.com

Website: www.physis.co.uk

I also keep a register of other qualified couples therapists and sex educators and love coaches whom I am prepared to recommend.

Anyone wanting to train as a Love Coach or Sex Educator should contact me by e-mail too. I run Certificate and Diploma courses for such people who are sincerely committed to the alleviation of human suffering and the promotion of human happiness. For themselves. And for other people.

CLARKSON INSTITUTE

SUMMARY OF NEW PARADIGM ADVANCED SEXUALITY CORE CONCEPTS:

- Orgasmic non-reproductive sex is NATURAL

- Ecstatic orgasmic sex involves sensations, emotions, communication (words & images) values, intelligence, imagination (fantasy & theories) as well as the soul.

- Only SAFE, SANE and CONSENSUAL SEX is ethical, moral and legal.

- The very best ecstatic sex happens in the best loving relationships.

- Use only up-to date scientifically correct anatomy for understanding sexual function.

- Beware of misinformed and misinforming medical or counselling practitioners !

- Lover and Beloved Orgasmic Power Sexplay is best for people to achieve ecstatic multiple orgasms which lead to altered brain states of long duration. (Usually kicks in only after 20 minutes of orgasm)

- Two hour weekly erotic Love Practice sex sessions *in the morning* when both men's and women's sexual hormones peak (and there's less likelihood of alcohol being consumed).

- Follow energy cycles e.g Remember the 50 minute brain cycle, 10 minute breaks

- Female Multiple orgasms – best techniques - *men* want to learn these

- Male Multiple orgasms – best techniques – *women* want to learn these

- Most so-called sexual 'problems' or 'dysfunctions' are the result of misinformation, NOT individual pathology or bad past experiences.

- Sex is not about 'the discharge of a drive', it's about the human organism's need for INTENSITY – feeling fully **alive** at all levels.

- Intensity is achieved by strongly contrasting experiences.

- Like any sport or art, becoming a champion lover depends on practice and professional coaching. Choose the league in which you want to play yourself........

- Finally, your sexuality is not defined by who you make love with, but by who you *are.*

THE CLARKSON INSTITUTE ADVANCED SEXUALITY RECOGNITION SYSTEM
(or Licenced to love.......)

The Clarkson Institute Advanced Sexuality Recognition System *(Or Licenced To Love.......)* is a way I'm developing for people who want to have a measure of what they have, and can, achieve in terms of understanding, experiencing, coaching and teaching Natural Ecstatic Human Sexuality.

It's STRUCTURE is based on the Clarkson Seven Level Model which *simultaneously* includes the physiological, emotional, communicative, ethical, rational, imaginative and transpersonal levels of human experience (ontology) **and** human knowledge (epistemology).

It's CONTENT is the best current information about creativity, healing, learning, human sexuality and our *relationships* at home and at work.

It's AIM is the achievement of the fullest sexual and relational potential of any individual Life.

It's OBJECTIVE is to make a global contribution to the alleviation of human suffering and the enhancement of human happiness.

White belt	Physiological sexual intelligence +
Orange belt	Emotional sexual intelligence +
Yellow belt	Communicative sexual intelligence +
Green belt	Ethical sexual intelligence +
Purple belt	Cognitive sexual intelligence + Advanced Sexuality Master+
Brown belt	Imaginative sexual intelligence + Apprentice Advanced Sexuality Coach +
Black belt	Spiritual sexual intelligence +

CERTIFICATION AS CLARKSON INSTITUTE CERTIFIED ADVANCED SEXUALITY COACH

If you want to know more about it, please just enquire.

INSTANTES (Moments)
Jorge Luis Borges

If I could live my life anew
In the next I'd try to make more mistakes.
I wouldn't try to be so perfect, I would relax more.
I would be more foolish than I've been, and of course I would
take very few things seriously. I would be less hygienic.
I would run more risks, make more voyages, contemplate more
sunsets, climb more mountains, swim more rivers.
I would go to more places I have never been before, have more
ice creams and fewer beans, I would have more real problems
and fewer imaginary ones.

I was one of those people who lived sensibly and prolifically
every moment of his life; of course I had moments of joy.
But if I could go back I would try to have only good moments,
For in case you didn't know it, that is what life is made of: only
of moments. Don't lose the now.
I was one of those who never went anywhere without a
thermometer, a hot water bottle, an umbrella and a parachute; If
I could live again, I would travel lighter.

If I could live my life anew I would start walking barefoot at the
beginning of spring and continue like that until Autumn had
ended.
I would have more rides on the merry-go-round, contemplate
more dawns and play with more children, if I had once more my
life before me.
But you see, I am 85 years old and I know that I am dying.

About the author

Professor Petruska Clarkson
D. Litt. et Phil, Ph.D., Ph.D (submitted), FBPS, FBACP.
is a Consultant Philosopher, Sexologist, BPS Chartered Psychologist (organisational, counselling and clinical), UKCP registered Psychotherapist, (qualified in individual, child, couples, sex and group psychotherapy), Research Psychologist, Recognised Psychoanalytic and Psychodynamic Supervisor (BAPPS) and Chartered Management Consultant (IMC) with some 30 years' international experience, who has more than 200 professional publications (23 languages) in these fields. She is also a poet, a qualified Reiki Master, a parfumier and is extremely skilled in facilitating others into writing and publishing their work - as well as achieving their other unique personal and professional goals.

Petruska will soon have three academic doctorates – one in *Relationship Psychology*. (The next one is in Positive Sexology.) She leads a **Transdisciplinary Professional Doctorate Programme** and other trainings and supervision as well as educational workshops (individual and groups) for the general public from PHYSIS, 58 Harley Street, London. e-mail: petruska.c@dial.pipex.com. www.physis.co.uk.

Petruska has had extensive training and supervision and been in teaching/supervisory positions for decades (and/or had *personal* experience of therapy) in all the major 'schools': Psychoanalysis, Jungian analysis, Cognitive Behavioural Therapy, Advanced Cognitive Behaviour Therapy, Rational Emotive Therapy, Personal Construct Therapy, Family Therapy, Sex Therapy, Crisis Intervention and Solution-focused, Systemic (and Narrative) Approaches, Rogerian Person-centred Approaches, Integrative

Psychotherapy, Phenomenology and Existentialist Approaches, Humanistic approaches, Tavistock, Relational and Interpersonal approaches, Hypnotherapy, Transpersonal psychotherapy approaches, Psychodrama, Creative Arts Therapies, Multi-cultural approaches, Gestalt and Experiential approaches, Transactional Analysis (TA), Bioenergetics, Philosophical Counselling, NLP, EMDR, COACHING and **Positive Psychology.**

She has had a great deal of media experience frequently on radio and being quoted in the popular press (from The Times to Cosmopolitan) featured in web cast debates and internet sites (Ananova and Big Brother) and has appeared on various TV programmes (from Jon Snow's Channel 4 programme and Sky News to Trisha, Esther, Kilroy and Ruby Wax.)

*NOTE: Petruska does **not** currently do her work in Sex Education and Love Coaching as a psychologist, but in her capacity as a Consultant Philosopher and Sexologist.*

"Empty is the argument of the philosopher which does not relieve any human suffering."

Epicurus (341-271BCE)

References

Andahazi, F. (1997) The Anatomist, London: Black Swan.

Anderson, D. & Berman, M. Sex tips for Straight Women from a Gay Man. London: Thorsons.

Bodansky, S. & Bodansky V. (2000) Extended Massive Orgasm, London: Vermilion.

Catrall, K. & Levinson, M. (2002) Satisfaction – The Art of the Female Orgasm. London: Thorsons.

Clarkson, P. (2000) Everything you ever wanted to know about therapy and were afraid to ask... First published by PHYSIS in 1994, now available as a PHYSIS Know-How booklet or CD-ROM from www.nospine.com

Clarkson, P. (2002) How to handle a woman. A PHYSIS Know-How book or CD-ROM available from www.nospine.com Also available in Spanish & in Italian

Clarkson, P. (2001) Everything you ever wanted to know about being in a couple relationship and were afraid to ask... A PHYSIS Know-How booklet or CD-ROM available from www.nospine.com

Clarkson, P. (2002) Everything you ever wanted to know about communication and were afraid to ask... A PHYSIS Know-How booklet or CD-ROM available from www.nospine.com

Clarkson, P. (2002)– Overcoming the Secret Fear of Failure - The Achilles Syndrome. London: Vega. First published by Element Books in 1994. Translated into Korean, Slovenian, Finnish, Portuguese, Spanish, Swedish and quite a number of other languages. Do enquire....

Clarkson, P. (2002) 21st Century Sex – or Freud's Project for a Scientific Psychology, Lillith's daughters and Jocasta's sons.

Clarkson, P. (2003) Sex for Therapists and other human beings. Self and Society,

Clarkson, P. (2003) No sex please, we're counsellors! Counselling and Psychotherapy Journal. March 2003 Vol. 14, No. 2, p.12 – 17.

Friday, N. (1979) My Secret Garden, London: Quartet.

Janus, S., & Janus, C., (1995) The Janus Report on Sexual Behaviour: The First Broadscale Scientific National Survey since Kinsey, New York: John Wiley.

Judson, O. (2002) <u>Dr Tatiana's Sex Advice to All Creation – The Definitive Guide to the Evolutionary Biology of Sex.</u> London: Chatto and Windus.

Kobelt, G.L. (1978) The Female Sex Organs in Humans and Some Mammals. (First published in German, 1844) in T.P. Lowry (ed) <u>The Classic Clitoris – Historic Contributions to Scientific Sexuality.</u> Chicago: Nelson-Hall p. 19 – 56, p.47.

O'Connell, Helen E., Hutson, John M., Anderson, Colin R. & Plenter, Robert J. (1998) Anatomical relationship between urethra and clitoris, <u>Journal of Urology,</u> 159(6), pp. 1892-1897.

Owen, T. (2002) Practical Suggestions. Published by the Outsider's Trust. P.O. Box 28724, London, E18 1XW.

Low, L.& Smith, T. (eds) <u>Understanding Sex</u>. The British Medical Association.

Paget, L. (2000) <u>How to give her Absolute Pleasure</u>. New York: Random House, & London: Piatkus.

The Kama Sutra of Vatsyana . Available in many editions in most good bookstores.

World Health Organization (1974) Please refer to:
www.who.int/health_topics/sexual_health/en for WHO publications.

Selected Academic Clarkson Works

Clarkson, P. (2002) Physis – A Psychophilosophical Life Science Study of Autopoiesis in Psychoanalysis, Jungian Psychology and Other Psychotherapies. available from www.nospine.com

Clarkson: P. (2002) War, Bystanding and Hate - Why Category Errors Are Dangerous. Journal of Psychotherapy and Politics. London: Whurr.

Clarkson, P. (ed.) (1998b) Counselling Psychology: Integrating Theory, Research and Supervised Practice, London: Routledge. Clarkson, P. (1997c)

Clarkson, P. (1998) Supervision in counselling, psychotherapy and health: An intervention priority sequencing model, European Journal for Counselling, Psychotherapy and Health, 1(2): 195-212.

Clarkson, P. (1995) The Therapeutic Relationship London: Whurr. (This book plus accompanying research papers was awarded a Ph.D. from Surrey University, UK.) Clarkson, P. (1995) Change in Organisations, London: Whurr.

Clarkson, P. (1996) The Bystander: An End to Innocence in Human Relationships? London: Whurr.

Clarkson, P. (ed.) (1997) On the Sublime, London: Whurr.

Clarkson, P. (ed.) (1997e) Supervision: Psychoanalytic and Jungian Perspectives, London: Whurr.

Clarkson, P. (2000) Ethics: Working with Ethical and Moral Dilemmas in Psychotherapy, London: Whurr.

Clarkson, P. (2002) The Transpersonal Relationship – The Hidden Curriculum of Spirituality. London; Whurr.

Clarkson, P. (2002) 'Psychotherapy, Memories of Abuse and Intersubjectivity – an Epistemological Study with Clinical Implications'. In Clarkson, P. On Psychotherapy, Volume 2, chapter 4, p. 51 – 71

Clarkson, P. (2001) Philosophy of Science? Epistemological category errors in psychotherapy discourse

Clarkson, P. (2002) Racism in psychotherapy - Institutional and/or Individual? Journal of Psychotherapy and Politics. London: Whurr.

* WEEKEND SEX WORKSHOPS FOR MEN

* WEEKEND SEX WORKSHOPS FOR WOMEN

* INDIVIDUAL LOVE COACHING FOR MEN

* INDIVIDUAL LOVE COACHING FOR WOMEN

* Assessment and referrals

• Personal and professional development groups

* Counselling   *   Psychotherapy

* Consultancy

* Psychology   * Business

* Individuals   *Couples   *Children

• Organisations   * Communities

* Writing   * Talks   * Media work

• Training and Education

• Supervision of couples and sex therapists

• *e-mail education and supervision also available*

GOOD SEX APPEAL FOR RESEARCH FUNDING

I have discovered how both women and men can have multiple extended whole-body/soul ecstatic orgasms for hours and hours.

What I am teaching is well beyond Tantra and does not involve any ejaculatory control.

I think this capacity is in *every* body as a NATURAL REFLEX no matter how old or disabled they are. I am beginning to understand how and why it works.

I believe it is Physis (Nature's) freely available non-addictive natural built-in medicine for much of the pain and suffering we all experience as embodied human beings on earth.

1) We would like to interview anyone who already reliably has orgasms as described above;

2) Our preliminary pilot documentation needs to be extended to scientific brain imaging of the resultant ecstatic orgasmic state for independent verification ; *and*

3) MRI & CAT scanning (or better) of the anatomically correct female clitoris's movements in this extended multiple orgasmic ecstatic state.

If you can help *in any way* or bring this "good sex appeal" to the attention of doctors, researchers, funders, genuine patrons or philanthropists who might be able to assist, PLEASE do so a.s.a.p. by circulating this as widely as possible. (One never knows from which direction help may come.......)

Love,

Professor **Petruska Clarkson**
Ph.D., D.Litt et Phil, Ph.D.

58 Harley Street, London, W1G 9QB
petruska.c@dial.pipex.com

Printed in the United Kingdom
by Lightning Source UK Ltd.
9386000001B